PRENTICE HALL

THE AMERICAN NATION

Guided Reading and Review Workbook

Teacher's Edition

Prentice Hall

Needham, Massachusetts
Upper Saddle River, New Jersey
Glenview, Illinois

ISBN 0-13-067872-4

1 2 3 4 5 6 7 8 9 10   06 05 04 03 02

Unit 4 ★ An Era of Expansion

Unit 5 ★ Division and Reunion

Unit 6 ★ Transforming The Nation

Unit 7 ★ New Role For The Nation

Unit 8 ★ Prosperity, Depression, and War

Unit 9 ★ The Bold Experiment Continues

Success in social studies comes from doing three things well—reading, testing, and writing. The following pages present strategies to help you read for meaning, understand test questions, and write well.

Reading for Meaning

Do you have trouble remembering what you read? Here are some tips from experts that will improve your ability to recall and understand what you read:

BEFORE YOU READ

Preview the text to identify important information.
Like watching the coming attractions at a movie theater, previewing the text helps you know what to expect. Study the questions and strategies below to learn how to preview what you read.

Ask yourself these questions:	Use these strategies to find the answers:
• What is the text about?	Read the headings, subheadings, and captions. Study the photos, maps, tables, or graphs.
• What do I already know about the topic?	Read the questions at the end of the text to see if you can answer any of them.
• What is the purpose of the text?	Turn the headings into *who, what, when, where, why,* or *how* questions. This will help you decide if the text compares things, tells a chain of events, or explains causes and effects.

AS YOU READ

Organize information in a way that helps you see meaningful connections or relationships.

Taking notes as you read will improve your understanding. Use graphic organizers like the ones below to record the information you read. Study these descriptions and examples to learn how to create each type of organizer.

Sequencing

A **flowchart** helps you see how one event led to another. It can also display the steps in a process.

Use a flowchart if the text—
- tells about a chain of events.
- explains a method of doing something.

TIP▶ List the events or steps in order.

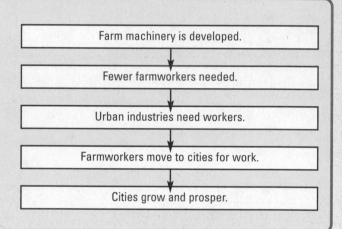

Farm machinery is developed.

↓

Fewer farmworkers needed.

↓

Urban industries need workers.

↓

Farmworkers move to cities for work.

↓

Cities grow and prosper.

Comparing and Contrasting

A **Venn diagram** displays similarities and differences.

Use a Venn diagram if the text—
- compares and contrasts two individuals, groups, places, things, or events.

TIP▶ Label the outside section of each circle and list differences.
Label the shared section and list similarities.

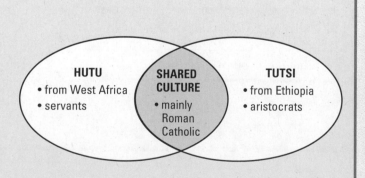

HUTU
- from West Africa
- servants

SHARED CULTURE
- mainly Roman Catholic

TUTSI
- from Ethiopia
- aristocrats

(continued)

Categorizing Information

A **chart** organizes information in categories.

Use a chart if the text—
- lists similar facts about several places or things.
- presents characteristics of different groups.

TIP▶ Write an appropriate heading for each column in the chart to identify its category.

COUNTRY	FORM OF GOVERNMENT	ECONOMY
Cuba	communist dictatorship	command economy
Puerto Rico	democracy	free enterprise system

Identifying Main Ideas and Details

A **concept web** helps you understand relationships among ideas.

Use a concept web if the text—
- provides examples to support a main idea.
- links several ideas to a main topic.

TIP▶ Write the main idea in the largest circle. Write details in smaller circles and draw lines to show relationships.

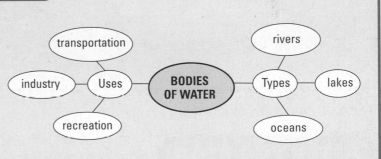

Organizing Information

An **outline** provides an overview, or a kind of blueprint for reading.

Use an outline to organize ideas—
- according to their importance.
- according to the order in which they are presented.

TIP▶ Use Roman numerals for main ideas, capital letters for secondary ideas, and Arabic numerals for supporting details.

> **I. Differences Between the North and the South**
> **A.** Views on slavery
>   **1.** Northern abolitionists
>   **2.** Southern slave owners
> **B.** Economies
>   **1.** Northern manufacturing
>   **2.** Southern agriculture

Identifying Cause and Effect

A **cause-and-effect** diagram shows the relationship between what happened (effect) and the reason why it happened (cause).

Use a cause-and-effect chart if the text—
- lists one or more causes for an event.
- lists one or more results of an event.

TIP▶ Label causes and effects. Draw arrows to indicate how ideas are related.

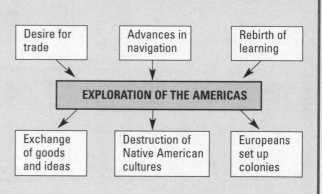

AFTER YOU READ

Test yourself to find out what you learned from reading the text.

Go back to the questions you asked yourself before you read the text. You should be able to give more complete answers to these questions:
- What is the text about?
- What is the purpose of the text?

You should also be able to make connections between the new information you learned from the text and what you already knew about the topic.

Study your graphic organizer. Use this information as the *answers*. Make up a meaningful *question* about each piece of information.

Taking Tests

Do you panic at the thought of taking a standardized test? Here are some tips that most test developers recommend to help you achieve good scores.

MULTIPLE-CHOICE QUESTIONS

Read each part of a multiple-choice question to make sure you understand what is being asked.

Many tests are made up of multiple-choice questions. Some multiple-choice items are **direct questions.** They are complete sentences followed by possible answers, called distractors.

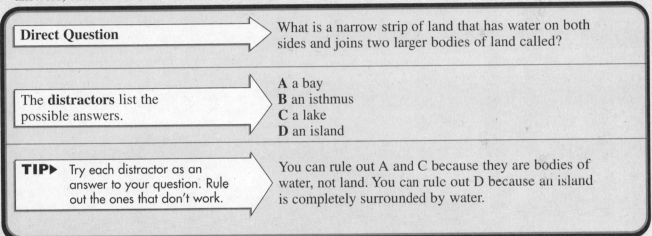

Direct Question	What is a narrow strip of land that has water on both sides and joins two larger bodies of land called?
The **distractors** list the possible answers.	**A** a bay **B** an isthmus **C** a lake **D** an island
TIP▶ Try each distractor as an answer to your question. Rule out the ones that don't work.	You can rule out A and C because they are bodies of water, not land. You can rule out D because an island is completely surrounded by water.

Other multiple-choice questions are **incomplete sentences** that you are to finish. They are followed by possible answers.

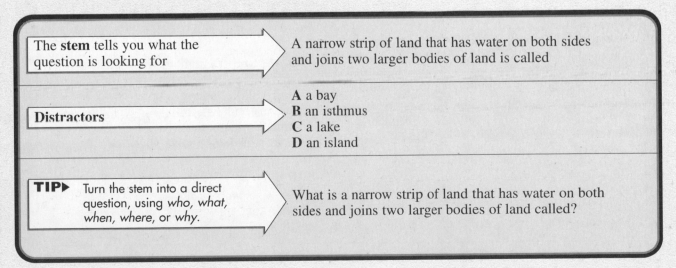

The **stem** tells you what the question is looking for	A narrow strip of land that has water on both sides and joins two larger bodies of land is called
Distractors	**A** a bay **B** an isthmus **C** a lake **D** an island
TIP▶ Turn the stem into a direct question, using *who, what, when, where,* or *why.*	What is a narrow strip of land that has water on both sides and joins two larger bodies of land called?

WHAT'S BEING TESTED?

Identify the type of question you are being asked.

Social studies tests often ask questions that involve reading comprehension.
Other questions may require you to gather or interpret information from a
map, graph, or chart. The following strategies will help you answer different
kinds of questions.

Reading Comprehension Questions

What to do:

How to do it:

1. Determine the content and organization
   of the selection.

   Read the **title.** Skim the selection. Look
   for key words that indicate time, cause-
   and-effect, or comparison.

2. Analyze the questions.
   Do they ask you to *recall facts?*

   Look for **key words** in the stem:
   According to the selection . . .
   The selection states that . . .

   Do they ask you to *make judgments?*

   The main idea of the selection is . . .
   The author would likely agree that . . .

3. Read the selection.

   Read quickly. Keep the questions in mind.

4. Answer the questions.

   Try out each distractor and choose
   the best answer. Refer back to the
   selection if necessary.

Example:
A Region of Diversity The Khmer empire was
one of many kingdoms in Southeast Asia. Unlike
the Khmer empire, however, the other kingdoms
were small because Southeast Asia's mountains
kept people protected and apart. People had little
contact with those who lived outside their own
valley.

Why were most kingdoms in Southeast
Asia small?
A disease killed many people
B lack of food
C climate was too hot
D mountains kept people apart

TIP▶ The key word because tells why the kingdoms were small.
(The correct answer is D.)

Map Questions

What to do:	How to do it:
1. Determine what kind of information is presented on the map.	Read the map **title.** It will indicate the purpose of the map. Study the **map key.** It will explain the symbols used on the map. Look at the **scale.** It will help you calculate distance between places on the map.
2. Read the question. Determine which component on the map will help you find the answer.	Look for **key words** in the stem. About <u>how far</u> . . . [use the scale] <u>What crops</u> were grown in . . . [use the map key]
3. Look at the map and answer the question in your own words.	Do not read the distractors yet.
4. Choose the best answer.	Decide which distractor agrees with the answer you determined from the map.

Eastern Europe: Language Groups

In which of these countries are Thraco-Illyrian languages spoken?

A Romania
B Albania
C Hungary
D Lithuania

TIP▶ Read the labels and the key to understand the map.
(The correct answer is B.)

KEY

☐ Slavic languages
☐ Romance languages
☐ Thraco-Illyrian languages
☐ Baltic languages
☐ Non-Indo-European languages

Lambert Azimuthal Equal-Area Projection

Graph Questions

What to do:

1. Determine the purpose of the graph.

2. Determine what information on the graph will help you find the answer.

3. Choose the best answer.

How to do it:

Read the graph **title.** It indicates what the graph represents.

Read the **labels** on the graph or on the key. They tell the units of measurement used by the graph.

Decide which distractor agrees with the answer you determined from the graph.

Example

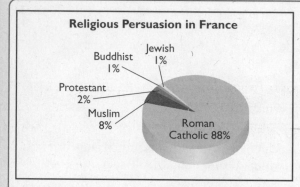

Religious Persuasion in France

Jewish 1%
Buddhist 1%
Protestant 2%
Muslim 8%
Roman Catholic 88%

A **Circle graph** shows the relationship of parts to the whole in terms of percentages.

After Roman Catholics, the next largest religious population in France is
A Buddhist   C Jewish
B Protestant   D Muslim

TIP▶ Compare the percentages listed in the labels.
(The correct answer is D.)

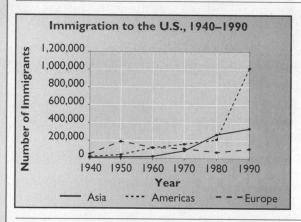

Immigration to the U.S., 1940–1990

Number of Immigrants

1,200,000
1,000,000
800,000
600,000
400,000
200,000
0

1940 1950 1960 1970 1980 1990
Year

—— Asia   ···· Americas   – – Europe

A **line graph** shows a pattern or change over time by the direction of the line.

Between 1980 and 1990, immigration to the U.S. from the Americas
A decreased a little   C stayed about the same
B increased greatly   D increased a little

TIP▶ Compare the vertical distance between the two correct points on the line graph.
(The correct answer is B.)

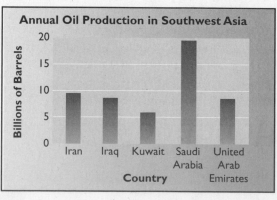

Annual Oil Production in Southwest Asia

Billions of Barrels

20
15
10
5
0

Iran   Iraq   Kuwait   Saudi Arabia   United Arab Emirates
Country

A **bar graph** compares differences in quantity by showing bars of different lengths.

Saudi Arabia produces about how many more billion of barrels of oil a year than Iran?
A 5 million   C 15 million
B 10 million   D 20 million

TIP▶ Compare the heights of the bars to find the difference.
(The correct answer is B.)

Writing for Social Studies

When you face a writing assignment, do you think, "How will I ever get through this?" Here are some tips to guide you through any writing project from start to finish.

THE WRITING PROCESS

Follow each step of the writing process to communicate effectively.

Step 1. Prewrite

- Establish the purpose.
- Define the topic.
- Determine the audience.
- Gather details.

Step 2. Draft

- Organize information logically in an outline or graphic organizer.
- Write an introduction, body, and conclusion.
- State main ideas clearly.
- Include relevant details to support your ideas.

Step 3. Revise

- Edit for clarity of ideas and elaboration.

Step 4. Proofread

- Correct any errors in spelling, grammar, and punctuation.

Step 5. Publish and Present

- Copy text neatly by hand, or use a typewriter or word processor.
- Illustrate as needed.
- Create a cover, if appropriate.

TYPES OF WRITING FOR SOCIAL STUDIES

Identify the purpose for your writing.

Each type of writing assignment has a specific purpose, and each purpose needs a different plan for development. The following descriptions and examples will help you identify the three purposes for social studies writing. The lists of steps will help you plan your writing.

Writing to Inform

Purpose: to present facts or ideas

Example

During the 1960s, research indicated the dangers of the insecticide DDT. It killed insects but also had long-term effects. When birds and fish ate poisoned insects, DDT built up in their fatty tissue. The poison also showed up in human beings who ate birds and fish contaminated by DDT.

TIP▶ Look for these **key terms** in the assignment: explain, describe, report, narrate

How to get started:
• Determine the topic you will write about.
• Write a topic sentence that tells the main idea.
• List all the ideas you can think of that are related to the topic.
• Arrange the ideas in logical order.

Writing to Persuade

Purpose: to influence someone

Example

Teaching computer skills in the classroom uses time that could be spent teaching students how to think for themselves or how to interact with others. Students who can reason well, express themselves clearly, and get along with other people will be better prepared for life than those who can use a computer.

TIP▶ Look for these **key terms** in the assignment: convince, argue, request

How to get started:
• Make sure you understand the problem or issue clearly.
• Determine your position.
• List evidence to support your arguments.
• Predict opposing views.
• List evidence you can use to overcome the opposing arguments.

Writing to Provide Historical Interpretations

Purpose: to present the perspective of someone in a different era

Example

The crossing took a week, but the steamship voyage was hard. We were cramped in steerage with hundreds of others. At last we saw the huge statue of the lady with the torch. In the reception center, my mother held my hand while the doctor examined me. Then, my father showed our papers to the official, and we collected our bags. I was scared as we headed off to find a home in our new country.

TIP▶ Look for these **key terms** in the assignment: go back in time, create, suppose that, if you were

How to get started:
• Study the events or issues of the time period you will write about.
• Consider how these events or issues might have affected different people at the time.
• Choose a person whose views you would like to present.
• Identify the thoughts and feelings this person might have experienced.

RESEARCH FOR WRITING

Follow each step of the writing process to communicate effectively.

After you have identified the purpose for your writing, you may need to do research. The following steps will help you plan, gather, organize, and present information.

Step 1. Ask Questions

Ask yourself questions to help guide your research.	What do I already know about the topic? What do I want to find out about the topic?

Step 2. Acquire Information

Locate and use appropriate sources of information about the topic.	Library Internet search Interviews
Take notes.	Follow accepted format for listing sources.

Step 3. Analyze Information

Evaluate the information you find.	Is it relevant to the topic? Is it up-to-date? Is it accurate? Is the writer an authority on the topic? Is there any bias?

Step 4. Use Information

Answer your research questions with the information you have found. (You may find that you need to do more research.)	Do I have all the information I need?
Organize your information into the main points you want to make. Identify supporting details.	Arrange ideas in outline form or in a graphic organizer.

Step 5. Communicate What You've Learned

	Purpose	Presentation
Review the purpose for your writing and choose an appropriate way to present the information.	inform	formal paper, documentary, multimedia
	persuade	essay, letter to the editor, speech
	interpret	journal, newspaper account, drama
Draft and revise your writing, and then evaluate it.	Use a rubric for self-evaluation.	

EVALUATING YOUR WRITING

Use the following rubric to help you evaluate your writing.

	Excellent	Good	Acceptable	Unacceptable
Purpose	Achieves purpose—to inform, persuade, or provide historical interpretation—very well	Informs, persuades, or provides historical interpretation reasonably well	Reader cannot easily tell if the purpose is to inform, persuade, or provide historical interpretation	Lacks purpose
Organization	Develops ideas in a very clear and logical way	Presents ideas in a reasonably well-organized way	Reader has difficulty following the organization	Lacks organization
Elaboration	Explains all ideas with facts and details	Explains most ideas with facts and details	Includes some supporting facts and details	Lacks supporting details
Use of Language	Uses excellent vocabulary and sentence structure with no errors in spelling, grammar, or punctuation	Uses good vocabulary and sentence structure with very few errors in spelling, grammar, or punctuation	Includes some errors in grammar, punctuation, and spelling	Includes many errors in grammar, punctuation, and spelling

Name _____ Class _____ Date _____

Section 1 Guided Reading and Review
Thinking Geographically

A. As You Read
Directions: Complete the chart below as you read Section 1 in your textbook. Fill in details about the five themes of geography. *Possible answers below*

The Five Themes of Geography	
1. location	Geographers use a grid of latitude and longitude to describe exact location. Relative location is the location of a place in relation to another place.
2. place	Physical features of a place include climate, soil, vegetation, animal life, and bodies of water. Human features include architecture, transportation systems, languages, and religions.
3. interaction	People adapt to and change their environment. Technology enables people to change their environment dramatically.
4. movement	The movement of people, goods, and ideas occurs because people and resources are unevenly distributed.
5. regions	Regions have unifying characteristics. These common characteristics may be physical or human and cultural.

B. Reviewing Key Terms
Directions: Explain how the following terms relate either to the five themes of geography or to maps and globes. *Possible answers below*

6. latitude   line that measures distance north or south of Equator; used to determine exact location

7. longitude   line that measures distance east or west of the Equator; used to determine exact location

8. natural resources   important aspect of place; environmental materials humans use to survive and meet needs

9. cartographer   a mapmaker

10. map projection   a way of showing the Earth on a flat surface

11. thematic map   a map that deals with a specific topic

CHAPTER

1

Section 2 Guided Reading and Review

Lands and Climates of the United States

A. Main Ideas

Directions: As you read Section 2 in your textbook, complete the chart with a brief description of each physical region or climate of the United States.

Physical Region	Climate
1. Pacific Coast westernmost region; includes high mountain ranges	9. marine southern Alaska to northern California; mild, moist climate
2. Intermountain Region east of Pacific Coast region; includes mountains, plateaus, canyons, deserts	10. Mediterranean California; mild, wet winters and hot, dry summers
3. Rocky Mountains mountainous range from Alaska through Canada into New Mexico	11. highland Cascades, Sierra Nevada, and Rocky Mountains; cooler temperatures
4. Interior Plains large lowland area between Rocky Mountains and Appalachian Mountains; rich in resources and fertile soil	12. desert/steppe desert: southwestern states west of the Rocky Mountains; hot days, cold nights, dry; steppe: Great Plains east of the Rocky Mountains; hot summers, cold winters, limited rainfall
5. Appalachian Mountains low, heavily forested eastern mountain range extending from Canada to Georgia and Mississippi	13. humid continental central plains and Northeast; mild summers, cold winters; more precipitation than steppe
6. Canadian Shield lowlands area mostly in eastern Canada that extends into Michigan, Wisconsin, and Minnesota	14. tropical/humid subtropical tropical: southern Florida and Hawaii; hot and humid; humid subtropical: southeastern states; warm temperatures, regular rainfall
7. Coastal Plains easternmost region; includes Atlantic Plain and Gulf Plain	15. tundra/subarctic tundra: northern and western coasts of Alaska; cold year round; subarctic: rest of Alaska and northern Canada; long, cold winters and short summers
8. Hawaiian Islands volcanic islands in the Pacific Ocean; dense, tropical rain forest	

B. Reviewing Key Terms

Directions: Match the terms in Column I with the descriptions in Column II. Write the letter of the correct answer in the space provided.

Column I

_c_ 16. isthmus

_d_ 17. erosion

_e_ 18. tributary

_a_ 19. precipitation

_b_ 20. altitude

Column II

a. rain, snow, sleet, or hail

b. height of the land above sea level

c. narrow strip of land

d. gradual wearing away of land

e. stream or river that flows into a larger river

Guided Reading and Review

Name _____ Class _____ Date _____

CHAPTER

1

Section 3 Guided Reading and Review
The Tools of History

A. As You Read

Directions: As you read Section 3 in your textbook, correct each of the following false statements. *Possible answers below*

1. A secondary source is firsthand information about people or events.

   <u>A primary source is firsthand information about people or events.</u>

2. A historian must first determine if a primary source is historic.

   <u>A historian must first determine if a primary source is authentic.</u>

3. When evaluating authenticity, a historian must look for bias.

   <u>When evaluating reliability, a historian must look for bias.</u>

4. History is the study of evidence left by early people and civilizations.

   <u>Archaeology is the study of evidence left by early people and civilizations.</u>

5. Historians never study ordinary people who do the everyday things that shape the community.

   <u>Historians study ordinary people who do the everyday things that shape the community.</u>

6. Absolute chronology shows the time of an event in relation to other events.

   <u>Relative chronology shows the time of an event in relation to other events.</u>

B. Reviewing Key Terms

Directions: Define the following terms.

7. bias   <u>leaning toward or against a certain person, group, or idea</u>

8. artifact   <u>object made by a human</u>

9. archaeology   <u>study of evidence left by early people</u>

10. culture   <u>way of life that a people has developed</u>

11. chronology   <u>sequence of events over time</u>

Name _____ Class _____ Date _____

CHAPTER

1

Section 4 Guided Reading and Review
Economics and Other Social Sciences

A. As You Read

Directions: As you read Section 4 in your textbook, complete the chart below by writing supporting details under each main idea. *Possible answers below*

Main Idea A: There are three basic economic questions each society must answer.

1. What goods and services should we produce?

2. How should we produce goods and services?

3. For whom should we produce goods and services?

Main Idea B: The American economic system is based on free enterprise.

4. In a free enterprise system, the government plays a limited role in the economy.

5. The founders believed that the prosperity of the nation depended on a free market economy.

Main Idea C: Other social sciences besides economics are important to the study of history.

6. Political science is the study of government.

7. Civics is the study of the rights and duties of citizens.

8. Anthropology, sociology, and psychology study people and the way they behave.

B. Reviewing Key Terms

Directions: Complete each sentence below by writing the correct term in the blank.

9. The study of how people manage their limited resources to satisfy their wants and needs is called _____ economics _____.

10. A _____ cash economy _____ is based on the exchange of money for goods and services.

11. _____ Civics _____ is the study of the rights and responsibilities of citizens.

12. The study of how peoples and cultures develop is called _____ anthropology _____.

Name _____ Class _____ Date _____

2 Section 1 Guided Reading and Review

The First Civilizations of the Americas

A. As You Read

Directions: Complete the chart below as you read Section 1 in your textbook. Fill in details about each civilization. *Possible answers below*

1. Olmec	farming civilization in Central America along the Gulf of Mexico; studied astronomy and developed a calendar; carved stone
2. Maya	farming civilization in rain forests of Guatemala and Mexico; social classes ranked by occupation; studied astronomy and mathematics
3. Aztec	civilization in central Mexico; built cities, causeways, and canals; studied astronomy and developed calendars; ruled a huge empire
4. Inca	largest empire in the Americas along west coast of South America; built magnificent capital city and many roads; strong central government ruled by emperor
5. Southwestern	Hohokams and Anasazi; southwestern United States; irrigated desert for farming; built roads and adobe buildings
6. Mound Builders	central and southern United States; farming culture; built large mounds of earth

B. Reviewing Key Terms

Directions: Define the following terms.

7. surplus *extra* _____

_____

8. quipu *string or cord with knots that stood for quantities* _____

_____

9. terrace *wide steps of land on which Incans farmed* _____

_____

10. pueblo *house built of adobe* _____

_____

CHAPTER

2

Section 2 Guided Reading and Review
Native American Cultures

A. As You Read

Directions: As you read Section 2 in your textbook, cross out the term or name that does not belong in each group below. Then explain how the remaining terms are related.

1. driftwood   pit houses   seal oil   ~~corn~~

   The remaining terms are all items from Inuit culture.

   _____

2. potlatch   ~~buffalo~~   canoes   villages

   The remaining terms are all from the culture of the Pacific Northwest.

   _____

3. calendar   Natchez   ~~igloo~~   Stinkard

   The remaining terms are all related to the Natchez culture.

   _____

4. ~~adobe~~   tepees   buffalo   Great Plains

   The remaining terms are all related to Great Plains peoples.

   _____

5. long house   confederacy   maple sugar   ~~kachina~~

   The remaining terms are all related to the Iroquois culture.

   _____

B. Reviewing Key Terms

Directions: Match the terms in Column I with the descriptions in Column II. Write the letter of the correct answer in the space provided.

Column I

_b_ 6. tribe

_c_ 7. pit house

_d_ 8. kachina

_a_ 9. clan

_e_ 10. sachem

Column II

a. group of related families

b. community of people that share common customs, language, and rituals

c. house dug into the ground and covered with wood and skins

d. spirit represented by a masked dancer

e. Iroquois tribal leader

Guided Reading and Review

CHAPTER

2

Section 3 Guided Reading and Review

Trade Networks of Africa and Asia

A. As You Read

Directions: As you read Section 3 in your textbook, answer the following questions.

1. Why do the 1400s mark the beginning of the first global age? At this time, international

   trade and travel increased dramatically.

2. Who founded Islam, and what do Muslims believe? Islam was founded by the prophet

   Muhammad. Its followers believe in one God.

3. How was the growth of trade in the Middle East linked to the growth of Islam?

   Muslim merchants took their faith to people along Asian and African trade routes.

4. What were the major trade routes Muslim traders traveled? They sailed to ports

   around the Indian Ocean. They traveled overland to China by the Silk Road.

5. What are some aspects of African village life? Villages are small. The people fish, herd, or farm.

   Many households include extended families. Kinship ties strengthen a sense of community.

6. Why did China not trade with outsiders until 1402? Most Chinese emperors before this time

   had been suspicious of outsiders. The emperor who came to power in 1402 was eager to trade with the rest of the world.

B. Reviewing Key Terms

Directions: Complete each sentence below by writing the correct term in the blank.

7. Muslims practice a religion called _____Islam_____, which was founded by the prophet Muhammad.

8. The _____Quran_____ is the sacred book of Islam.

9. The _____Silk Road_____ was an overland trade route that linked China and the Middle East.

10. _____Caravans_____ were groups of people who traveled together for safety.

11. A _____city-state_____ is a large town whose government controls the surrounding countryside.

12. Several generations of an _____extended family_____ live in one household.

CHAPTER

2

Section 4 Guided Reading and Review
Tradition and Change in Europe

A. As You Read

Directions: As you read Section 4 in your textbook, complete the chart below by writing supporting details under each main idea. *Possible answers below*

Main Idea A: Judaism and Christianity, two religions of the ancient Middle East, shaped European beliefs.

1. _Judaism refers to the beliefs of the Israelites; they believed in one God and in the duty to obey God's rules._

2. _Jesus, a Jewish prophet, inspired a new religion called Christianity, whose followers called him Messiah._

3. _Christianity became the official religion of Rome, and Christians sent out missionaries across Europe._

Main Idea B: The customs of two ancient civilizations, Greece and Rome, shaped European traditions.

4. _Greeks valued human reason and created the first direct democracy._

5. _Rome was a republic that covered much of modern western Europe and lasted almost 500 years._

Main Idea C: The Middle Ages was a transition from the decline of the Roman empire to the modern era.

6. _Invasion and war were common during the Middle Ages._

7. _The manor was the center of feudal society in the Middle Ages._

Main Idea D: The Renaissance expanded European geographical and intellectual horizons.

8. _Scholars studied ancient writings and began making their own discoveries._

9. _The printing press made it possible to spread learning more quickly._

10. _Trade brought new prosperity, and explorers began crossing the Atlantic._

B. Reviewing Key Terms

Directions: Define each term below, and identify the civilization or era with which it is associated: Jewish, Christian, Greek, Roman, Middle Ages, or Renaissance.

11. salvation _Christian; everlasting life_

12. missionary _Christian; people who spread Christian teachings across Europe_

13. direct democracy _Greek; form of government in which ordinary citizens have the power to govern_

14. republic _Roman; a system of government in which citizens choose representatives to govern them_

15. feudalism _Middle Ages; system of rule by nobles who ruled their lands but owed loyalty and military service to a monarch_

16. manor _Middle Ages; a lord's castle and the lands around it_

17. Crusades _Christian; holy wars fought in the Middle East that greatly expanded European trade with the East_

18. astrolabe _Middle Ages; an instrument that helps sailors determine their latitude while at sea_

Name _____ Class _____ Date _____

Section 1 Guided Reading and Review
An Era of Exploration

A. As You Read

Directions: Complete the chart below as you read Section 1 in your textbook. Fill in the missing causes and effects. *Possible answers below*

Causes	Effects
1. Vikings sailed to North America and settled there for a time.	Vikings left behind detailed records of their voyages.
Spain wanted a share of the Asian spice trade.	2. Ferdinand and Isabella agreed to sponsor voyages of exploration to the west.
Columbus returned to Spain with exotic gifts such as parrots and pearls.	3. His success made the king and queen agree to finance more voyages west.
4. Europeans brought diseases to which the Taino had never been exposed.	Contact with the Europeans wiped out much of the Taino population of the West Indies.
5. Ferdinand Magellan's crew sailed all the way around the world.	Europeans learned the true size of the Earth.
Europeans brought the first horses to North America.	6. Native Americans began riding horses and using them to carry loads.

B. Reviewing Key People

Directions: Identify each of the following people. Include the country or region for which each sailed and the areas each explored, claimed, and/or settled.

7. Leif Ericson   Scandinavia; reached the northern tip of North America
_____

8. Christopher Columbus   Spain; explored the Caribbean islands and claimed them for Spain
_____

9. Vasco Núñez de Balboa   Spain; explored Panama and claimed the Pacific Ocean for Spain
_____

10. Ferdinand Magellan   Spain; first European to cross the Pacific Ocean
_____

CHAPTER

3 Section 2 Guided Reading and Review
Spain Builds an Empire

A. As You Read

Directions: As you read Section 2 in your textbook, answer each of the following questions.

1. What motivated the Spanish conquistadors to sail to the Americas? belief that they
   were serving God and the king; desire for gold

2. How were Cortés and Pizarro able to conquer the Aztecs and Incas? The Spaniards had
   guns and were protected by armor. They rode horses, animals the Americans had never seen before. The Aztecs
   thought the Spaniards were gods. The Spaniards brought diseases that killed the Indians.

3. What became of Álvar Núñez Cabeza de Vaca? He was captured by Indians but escaped and
   with three others traveled through the Southwest for three years.

4. Why did Spaniards, such as De Soto and Coronado, fail to settle North America?
   They were greedy for gold or other treasure. They were not interested in settling the land.

5. How did the king of Spain arrange for his new lands to be settled? He set up
   a strong system of government, appointing viceroys to each region. He wrote laws stating how the western
   colonies would be governed.

6. What were the four social classes in the Spanish colonies of North America?
   peninsulares, creoles, mestizos, Indians

7. Why did the Spaniards begin the Atlantic slave trade? Too many Indians were dying of
   hunger, disease, and mistreatment. A new source of workers was needed to work the plantations and mines.

B. Reviewing Key Terms

Directions: Define the following terms.

8. conquistador conqueror; leader of expeditions to the Americas, often appointed to rule newly conquered territory

9. pueblo town; center of farming and trade in New Spain

10. presidio forts where soldiers lived in New Spain

11. mission religious settlement run by Spanish Catholics; forced Indians to work

12. creole people born in the Americas to Spanish parents

13. mestizo people of mixed Spanish and Indian ancestry

14. encomienda land grant to settlers that included the right to demand labor or taxes from Native Americans

Name _____ Class _____ Date _____

3

Section 3 Guided Reading and Review

Colonizing North America

A. As You Read

Directions: As you read Section 3 in your textbook, mark each statement true or false. Correct each false statement.

true 1. John Cabot and a crew of English sailors thought they had discovered the Northwest Passage. _____

false 2. Giovanni da Verrazano sailed up the St. Lawrence River on a voyage sponsored by France. _____Jacques Cartier_____

true 3. Henry Hudson explored the Hudson River for the Dutch and the Hudson Bay for the English. _____

false 4. Supporters of Queen Elizabeth I are called Protestants.
_____Martin Luther of Germany_____

false 5. French explorer Jacques Cartier founded Port Royal and Quebec in Canada.
_____Samuel de Champlain_____

false 6. The French bought Manhattan Island from the local Indians.
_____Dutch_____

true 7. French and Dutch settlers in North America became rivals over the fur trade.
_____

B. Reviewing Key Terms

Directions: Use each term correctly in a sentence about the early French and Dutch settlement of North America. _Possible answers below_

8. Northwest Passage _the Northwest Passage was the name for the waterway through or around North_ _America that Europeans believed connected the Atlantic Ocean to Asia._

9. *coureur de bois* _A coureur debois was a French colonist who lived and worked in the Canadian woods._

10. missionary _Christian missionaries tried to convert Native Americans to their religiousbeliefs._

11. alliance _to obtain their help and protection, the Dutch and French settlers formed alliances with various_ _Native American peoples._

CHAPTER

3

Section 4 Guided Reading and Review

Building the Jamestown Colony

A. As You Read

Directions: As you read Section 4 in your textbook, complete each of the following sentences.

1. When Thomas Gates landed in Virginia in 1610, he found <u>60 starving colonists</u> <u>remaining of the original 700.</u>

2. Walter Raleigh sent John White to Roanoke in order to <u>reestablish the English colony there.</u>

3. The Virginia Company charter authorized <u>settlement of the land between present-day North</u> <u>Carolina and the Potomac River, and rights of English citizenship to the colonists who settled there.</u>

4. Captain John Smith was an effective leader because he <u>forced people to work for their</u> <u>food and formed alliances with local Indians.</u>

5. Jamestown began to prosper when the colonists <u>began to grow and export tobacco.</u>

6. The Virginia House of Burgesses was important because <u>it was the first example of</u> <u>representative government in the English colonies.</u>

B. Reviewing Key Terms

Directions: Define the following terms.

7. charter <u>a document giving certain rights to a person or company</u>

8. burgess <u>an elected representative to the government</u>

9. Magna Carta <u>also known as the Great Charter; a document that said the king could not raise taxes</u> <u>without first consulting a council of nobles and church leaders</u>

10. Parliament <u>a representative assembly that developed from the Great Council; organized into two houses,</u> <u>one of nobles and one of elected representatives</u>

CHAPTER

3 Section 5 Guided Reading and Review

Seeking Religious Freedom

A. As You Read

Directions: As you read Section 5 in your textbook, complete the chart below by writing supporting details for each main idea. *Possible answers below*

Main Idea A: It was not easy for people to practice religion freely in Europe during the 1500s.

1. European Protestants and Catholics fought religious wars.

2. Most European rulers supported particular religions and did not tolerate others.

3. People who did not practice the established state religion were often persecuted.

Main Idea B: Religious separatists decided to leave Europe and settle in North America.

4. English separatists first settled in Holland.

5. They wanted their children to grow up English.

6. They sailed for North America in 1620 to establish a colony.

Main Idea C: The Pilgrims' first years in North America were difficult.

7. The Pilgrims had not brought enough food to get them through the winter.

8. They did not have enough time to build proper shelters.

B. Reviewing Key Terms

Directions: Define the following terms.

9. **established church** a particular religion supported by the state

10. **persecution** mistreatment or punishment of certain people because of their beliefs

11. **Mayflower Compact** agreement for governing the Plymouth Colony signed by those who sailed to North America on the Mayflower

12. **precedent** example for others to follow in the future

Guided Reading and Review

Name _____ Class _____ Date _____

Section 1 Guided Reading and Review
The New England Colonies

A. As You Read

Directions: As you read Section 1 in your textbook, complete the chart below. Fill in key similarities and differences among the New England colonies of Massachusetts Bay, Connecticut, and Rhode Island. *Possible answers below*

Similarities
1. founded by settlers seeking religious freedom
2. peaceful relations with Indians at first; hostility began as more Europeans arrived and took over Indian lands
3. importance of Sabbath day
4. town meetings
5. rich in natural resources

Differences
6. Massachusetts Bay founded by Puritans; male church members allowed to vote; powerful governor
7. Connecticut founded by discontented colonists from Massachusetts Bay; all male property owners allowed to vote; governor's power limited
8. Rhode Island founded on principle of separation of church and state; full religious tolerance for Protestants, Jews, and Catholics; all white males allowed to vote

B. Reviewing Key People

Directions: Identify each of the following people.

9. Charles I   became King of England in 1625; anti-Puritan

10. John Winthrop   British lawyer and Puritan; first governor of Massachusetts Bay Colony

11. Thomas Hooker   Puritan minister who founded the colony of Connecticut

12. Roger Williams   Massachusetts minister who founded Rhode Island to establish religious tolerance

13. Anne Hutchinson   woman who held religious discussions with neighbors

14. Metacom   Wampanoag chief called "King Philip" by settlers; led attacks on colonial villages until his capture and death

Guided Reading and Review

Name _____ Class _____ Date _____

Section 2 Guided Reading and Review
The Middle Colonies

A. As You Read

Directions: As you read Section 2 in your textbook, complete the chart below by writing supporting details for each main idea. *Possible answers below*

Main Idea A: The Dutch colony of New Netherland became the English colony of New York.

1. _The Dutch settlers traded in furs and made the colony prosperous; England wanted to take it over._

2. _In 1664, English ships invaded New Amsterdam's harbor; Governor Peter Stuyvesant surrendered._

3. _The colony was renamed New York in honor of the Duke of York._

Main Idea B: New Jersey attracted settlers from many lands.

4. _The colony had fertile farmland and rich resources._

5. _New Jersey allowed religious freedom._

Main Idea C: Pennsylvania was founded as an experiment in religious tolerance.

6. _To protect his Quaker friend William Penn from persecution in England, King Charles II granted him a large tract of land in North America._

7. _Penn welcomed people of different religions to settle in Pennsylvania._

8. _This policy of religious tolerance attracted settlers from many countries._

B. Reviewing Key People and Terms

Directions: Identify each person or define each term below, and note whether it relates to New York, New Jersey, or Pennsylvania.

9. patroon   _New York; owner of a huge estate_

10. Peter Stuyvesant   _New York; Dutch governor of New Netherland who surrendered the colony to the English_

11. proprietary colony   _New Jersey; colony in which one or more people have been given the land by the king_

12. royal colony   _New Jersey; colony under control of the English crown_

13. Quaker   _Pennsylvania; Protestants who believed that all people were equal in God's sight_

14. Pennsylvania Dutch   _Pennsylvania; name given to German settlers of Pennsylvania because of a mispronunciation of the word Deutsch (German)_

CHAPTER

4

Section 3 Guided Reading and Review

The Southern Colonies

A. As You Read

Directions: As you read Section 3 in your textbook, mark each statement true or false. Correct each false statement.

__false__ 1. The Mason-Dixon Line marked the border between New England and the Middle Colonies. replace New England with Southern Colonies

__true__ 2. Maryland was founded as a Catholic colony. _____

__false__ 3. During Bacon's Rebellion, the city of Jamestown, Maryland, was burned.
replace Maryland with Virginia

__true__ 4. Slavery quickly become common in North Carolina and South Carolina because of the rice plantations. _____

__true__ 5. The first European settlers of Georgia were people who could not pay their debts. _____

__false__ 6. Most of the great plantations in the South were located in the backcountry at the base of the Appalachians. plantations were located in the Tidewater region

__true__ 7. Many Africans who became slaves in the colonies were captured and sold into slavery by other Africans. _____

B. Reviewing Key Terms

Directions: Match the terms in Column I with the descriptions in Column II. Write the letter of the correct answer in the space provided.

Column I

__c__ 8. Act of Toleration

__d__ 9. indigo

__a__ 10. debtor

__e__ 11. slave code

__b__ 12. racism

Column II

a. person who owes money

b. belief that one race is superior to another

c. law providing religious freedom to all Christians

d. plant used to make blue dye

e. laws that set out rules for slaves' behavior and denied their basic rights

Name _____ Class _____ Date _____

Section 4 Guided Reading and Review

Roots of Self-Government

A. As You Read

Directions: As you read Section 4 in your textbook, complete the chart below by writing supporting details under each main idea. *Possible answers below*

Main Idea A: England regulated trade with the North American colonies.

1. England believed that a nation remained strong by controlling its trade.

2. Parliament passed Navigation Acts meant to regulate trade between England and the colonies.

3. England benefited because no other countries could trade with the colonies.

4. The triangular trade took West Indian molasses to New England, goods from New England to West Africa, and enslaved Africans to the West Indies.

Main Idea B: Governments in all the colonies had certain characteristics in common.

5. Each colony had a governor; some were appointed and others were elected.

6. Each colony had a legislature to make its laws; the lower house of most legislatures was popularly elected.

7. White Christian men who were over 21 and owned property had the right to vote.

B. Reviewing Key Terms

Directions: Define the following terms.

8. mercantilism   *economic theory stating that a nation became strong by controlling trade*

9. export   *to sell goods outside a country*

10. triangular trade   *trade route that brought West Indian molasses to New England, goods from New England to West Africa, and enslaved Africans to the West Indies*

11. legislature   *a group of people with the power to make laws*

12. bill of rights   *a written list of freedoms a government promises to protect*

Name _____ Class _____ Date _____

4

Section 5 Guided Reading and Review

Life in the Colonies

A. As You Read

Directions: As you read Section 5 in your textbook, complete the following sentences.

1. The gentry of colonial society included <u>wealthy planters, merchants, ministers, lawyers, and royal officials.</u>

2. Women in the colonies worked at many jobs, including <u>raising children, keeping house, gardening, cooking, cleaning, making clothing, taking care of livestock, farming, or in such occupations as midwife, maid, cook, nurse, shoemaker, or printer.</u>

3. The Gullah language has its roots in <u>English and West African languages.</u>

4. Two effects of the Great Awakening were <u>to create splits in churches and to encourage challenges to authority.</u>

5. New Englanders believed in education for all children because <u>all people need to be able to read in order to study the Bible.</u>

6. The basic belief of the Enlightenment era was <u>that reason and scientific methods could be applied to the study of society.</u>

7. Benjamin Franklin's contributions to the city of Philadelphia included <u>printing the almanac and persuading officials to pave the streets, organize a fire company, and set up a lending library.</u>

8. The case of John Peter Zenger was important because <u>it established that the press was free to criticize the government.</u>

B. Reviewing Key Terms

Directions: Define the following terms.

9. middle class <u>farmers, skilled craftsworkers, and tradespeople</u>

10. indentured servant <u>person who agreed to work for a period of years for anyone who would pay for his or her ocean passage to the Americas</u>

11. apprentice <u>one who learns a trade from a master in exchange for room and board</u>

12. dame school <u>private school for girls run by a woman in her own home</u>

Guided Reading and Review

CHAPTER

5

Section 1 Guided Reading and Review
The French and Indian War

A. As You Read

Directions: Write the missing cause or effect as you read Section 1 in your textbook.
Possible answers below

1. Cause: French trappers and traders in North America adopted Native American Ways.	1. Effect The French built strong alliances with Native American groups.
2. Cause The Governor of Virginia sent Washington to build a fort in Ohio country.	2. Effect: Washington attacked the French but later surrendered.
3. Cause: General Braddock ignored warnings of Indian scouts near Fort Duquesne.	3. Effect The French launched a surprise attack, and many British were killed.
4. Cause William Pitt became head of the British government.	4. Effect: The best British generals were sent to North America.
5. Cause: The British won the Battle of Quebec.	5. Effect Conflict between French and British in North America ended.

B. Reviewing Key Places

Directions: Explain how each of the following places relates to the French and Indian War.

6. Ohio River   linked French land in Canada with French settlements along the Mississippi River

_____

7. Fort Duquesne   any of: location of defeat of General Braddock's troops; near site of first battle of the war;
   site of British victory near the end of the war

8. Louisbourg   most important French fort in Canada, captured by British

_____

9. Quebec   site of the final battle in North America and a French defeat

CHAPTER

5

Section 2 Guided Reading and Review

Turmoil Over Taxation

A. As You Read

Directions: As you read Section 2 in your textbook, answer the following questions:
Possible answers below

1. What was the cause of Pontiac's War? The British raised prices of goods and allowed settlement on Indian lands.

2. What did the Proclamation of 1763 state? It forbade colonists to settle west of the Appalachian Mountains and required any settlers already in the area to leave.

3. How did colonists react to the Proclamation of 1763? Why? They were angry because some colonies claimed western land and because they had to pay the cost of additional British troops.

4. Why did Parliament pass the Sugar Act? Britain was deep in debt because of the French and Indian War.

5. What reason did the colonists have for protesting the Stamp Act? Colonists cited the English tradition of "no taxation without representation."

6. What did the Townshend Acts create besides new taxes? legal documents called writs of assistance, which allowed customs officials to search without a reason

7. What activities did the Sons of Liberty and the Daughters of Liberty organize? protests, mock hangings, parades, petitions, boycotts

8. In what way did the Boston Massacre differ from earlier protests? British soldiers fired into the crowd, and five Americans were killed.

B. Reviewing Key People

Directions: Briefly identify each of the following people, and explain how each relates to the protests over taxes.

9. Samuel Adams Boston patriot; organized anti-British protests

10. Mercy Otis Warren playwright who used writing to encourage anti-British feelings; held meetings of anti-British colonists

11. Patrick Henry Virginia lawyer who gave anti-British speeches in the House of Burgesses

12. Crispus Attucks African American sailor killed in the Boston Massacre

13. Paul Revere Boston silversmith whose engraving of the Boston Massacre stirred up anti-British feelings

CHAPTER

5

Section 3 Guided Reading and Review

From Protest to Revolution

A. As You Read

Directions: Each of the following statements is either true or false. As you read Section 3 in your textbook, mark each statement true or false. If a statement is false, correct the statement.

	True or False	Correct Statement
1. Sons of Liberty supported the tea boycott by throwing British tea overboard.	true	
2. The British passed the Intolerable Acts in response to the Boston Massacre.	false	The British passed the Intolerable Acts in response to the Boston Tea Party.
3. Other colonies could not agree whether or not to support Boston after the passage of the Intolerable Acts.	false	Other colonies united in support of Boston after the passage of the Intolerable Acts.
4. The British marched on Concord to seize arms and ammunition.	true	
5. A professional colonial army opened fire on the British on Lexington Green.	false	A volunteer colonial army opened fire on the British on Lexington Green.

B. Reviewing Key Terms

Directions: Match the description in Column I with the terms in Column II. Write the letter of the correct answer in the space provided.

Column I

___c___ 6. dumping of three shiploads of tea into Boston Harbor

___a___ 7. meeting of representatives of all the colonies to decide on response to British policies

___b___ 8. made lands between Ohio and Missouri Rivers part of Quebec

Column II

a. First Continental Congress

b. Quebec Act

c. Boston Tea Party

CHAPTER

6

Section 1 Guided Reading and Review
Fighting Begins in the North

A. As You Read

Directions: As you read Section 1 in your textbook, use the letters A–D to label the following events in correct chronological order. Write a sentence or two explaining the importance of each event. *Possible answers below*

___D___ 1. the blockade of all colonial ports

The blockade stopped people and supplies from coming into or going out of the colonies.

_____

___B___ 2. the appointment of George Washington as Commander of the Continental Army

The army was disorganized and needed good leadership. Washington had led troops before.

_____

___C___ 3. the Battle of Bunker Hill

This was the first major battle of the Revolution. The battle showed that Americans were brave fighters.

The battle showed that the British would not be easy to defeat.

___A___ 4. the American victory at Fort Ticonderoga

The Americans gained a supply of cannons and gunpowder. The victory gave Americans control of an

important route to Canada.

B. Reviewing Key Terms

Directions: Complete the sentences in Column I with the terms in Column II. Write the letter of the correct term in the space provided.

Column I

___b___ 5. The request of Congress that King George repeal the Intolerable Acts was called the _____.

___d___ 6. The _____ was made up entirely of volunteers, most of whom had no military training or experience.

___a___ 7. A/An _____ was a colonist who supported Britain.

___c___ 8. When a/an _____ is set up, people and supplies cannot pass through a port.

Column II

a. Loyalist

b. Olive Branch Petition

c. blockade

d. Continental Army

Guided Reading and Review

CHAPTER

6

Section 2 Guided Reading and Review

The Colonies Declare Independence

A. As You Read

Directions: As you read Section 2 in your textbook, complete the chart below by writing three supporting details under each main idea. *Possible answers below*

Main Idea A: Certain natural rights belong to all people from birth.

1. All people are born equal and are entitled to life, liberty, and the pursuit of happiness.

2. People set up governments to protect their rights and liberties.

3. If government fails to protect people's rights, the people have the right to overthrow the government.

Main Idea B: Great Britain committed many wrongs against the colonies.

4. The king disbanded colonial legislatures.

5. Britain sent troops to the colonies during peacetime.

6. Britain taxed the colonists without their consent.

Main Idea C: The British colonies are now the United States of America.

7. The colonies have no further ties to Great Britain.

8. The United States is a free and independent nation.

9. The United States has the power to do all the things that independent states may do.

B. Reviewing Key Terms *Possible answers below*

Directions: Explain how each of the following relates to the American Revolution.

10. *Common Sense* This pamphlet by Thomas Paine urged the colonies to declare independence.

11. traitor Because the delegates declared independence, they were disloyal to Britain, and the British could hang them as traitors.

12. Declaration of Independence This document described the reasons for breaking away from Great Britain.

Name _____ Class _____ Date _____

6 Section 3 Guided Reading and Review

Struggles in the Middle States

A. As You Read

Directions: As you read Section 3 in your textbook, answer the following questions:

Possible answers below

1. What happened during the Battle of Long Island? General Howe's forces defeated General

   Washington's troops, and many Americans were killed.

2. Who was Nathan Hale? Hale was a Patriot spy who was captured and hanged.

   _____

3. What was the result of the American attack on Trenton? The Americans surprised the

   Hessian troops and took most of them prisoner.

4. How did the Americans defeat Cornwallis at Princeton? Washington left his campfires
   burning so that Cornwallis would think American troops had stopped for the night. Instead, they moved behind
   British lines in the dark and attacked British soldiers marching to Princeton.

5. What was General Burgoyne's plan of attack? Burgoyne planned to march on Albany from three

   directions. The British would then control the Hudson River, stopping the flow of soldiers and supplies to the Americans.

6. Why was the British defeat at Saratoga important? It ended the British threat to New England.

   It boosted American spirits. It convinced France to become an ally of the United States.

7. Name two Europeans who contributed to the American cause, and explain their

   contributions. Any two of the following: The Marquis de Lafayette brought trained soldiers to help

   Washington. Friedrich von Steuben helped train Washington's troops. Thaddeus Kosciusko helped build forts and

   other defenses. Casimir Pulaski trained cavalry troops.

8. Describe conditions at Valley Forge in the winter of 1777–1778. Soldiers stayed in

   damp, drafty huts or slept on frozen ground. Some had no shoes. They suffered frostbite and disease.

B. Reviewing Key Places and Terms

Directions: Identify each place, and define each term.

9. Battle of Long Island battle near New York City; a British victory

10. Battle of Trenton surprise American attack on Hessian soldiers; an American victory

11. Battle of Saratoga an American victory and major turning point in the war

12. allies nations that work together to achieve a common goal

13. cavalry troops on horseback

14. Valley Forge location where Washington's troops camped for the winter of 1777–1778

Guided Reading and Review

Name _____ Class _____ Date _____

CHAPTER

6

Section 4 Guided Reading and Review
Fighting for Liberty on Many Fronts

A. As You Read
Directions: As you read Section 4 in your textbook, complete the chart below by writing key supporting details under each main idea. *Possible answers below*

Main Idea A: American women played important roles in the war.

1. *When men left home for the army, women ran the farms and businesses.*
   Women went with their husbands in the army and nursed the wounded, washed clothes, cooked, and even took
2. *over firing guns.*

Main Idea B: Many African Americans served in the war.

3. *At least nine African American minutemen fought at Lexington and Concord.*

4. *African American soldiers formed special regiments, and some became spies.*

Main Idea C: Fierce battles were fought in the West.

5. *Americans had to fight against Native Americans who supported the British.*

6. *George Rogers Clark led successful attacks against the British in the Ohio Valley.*

Main Idea D: American ships struck some important blows for the Patriot cause.

7. *Captain John Paul Jones captured the British ship Serapis.*

B. Reviewing Key People
Directions: Briefly identify the following people. *Possible answers below*

8. Mary Ludwig Hays *was with her husband at the front; took over firing the cannon when he was wounded*
_____

9. Peter Salem *African American minuteman who fought at Lexington, Concord, and Bunker Hill*
_____

10. Joseph Brant *Mohawk leader who fought against the Patriots*
_____

11. George Rogers Clark *led Virginia frontier fighters against the British in the Ohio Valley*
_____

12. John Paul Jones *American navy captain who captured the British warship Serapis*
_____

Name _____ Class _____ Date _____

CHAPTER

6

Section 5 Guided Reading and Review

Winning the War in the South

A. As You Read

Directions: As you read Section 5 in your textbook, write the missing information under each heading.

Fighting in the South

1. The British decided to try to win the war in the South because many ____Loyalists____ lived in the southern colonies.

2. The Americans' greater knowledge of ____local geography____ put the British at a disadvantage in the South.

3. Two American generals who helped turn the tide in the southern battles were ____Nathanael Greene____ and ____Daniel Morgan____.

4. Francis Marion was called the ____Swamp Fox____ because of his surprise appearances, sudden attacks, and quick retreats.

Victory at Yorktown

5. General Cornwallis thought that if he conquered ____Virginia____, he would cut off American supply routes to the South.

6. ____Benedict Arnold____ was a skilled American general, but his name became a synonym for "traitor" when he agreed to turn over West Point to the British.

7. Retreating to Yorktown was a serious mistake for the British because Yorktown was on a/an ____peninsula____, and they were trapped with no means of retreat.

The Peace Treaty

8. The Treaty of Paris stated that the ____Mississippi River____ formed the western border of the United States.

B. Reviewing Key Terms

Directions: Match the descriptions in Column I with the terms in Column II. Write the letter of the correct answer in the space provided.

Column I

___b___ 9. army surrounds and blockades an enemy position

___c___ 10. approve

___a___ 11. hit-and-run tactics

Column II

a. guerrilla

b. siege

c. ratify

Guided Reading and Review

Name _____ Class _____ Date _____

Section 1 Guided Reading and Review
A Loose Confederation

A. As You Read
Directions: Complete the following sentences as you read Section 1 in your textbook.

1. Each state's constitution sets out *organization and processes of a government.*

2. In 1777, the Continental Congress approved *the Articles of Confederation.*

3. Compared with the states, under the Articles Congress had *very limited powers.*

4. Maryland demanded that other states cede their claims to western lands because *they feared the "landed" states would become too powerful.*

5. Disputes continued to arise among states because *the Articles did not give the central government the power to resolve the disputes.*

6. Without the power to tax, Congress *could not repay its debts.*

7. Britain refused to withdraw its troops from the Ohio Valley, and Spain *closed its port in New Orleans.*

8. Under the Land Ordinance of 1785, the Northwest Territory would be *surveyed and divided into townships.*

9. The Northwest Ordinance allowed a territory to request statehood if *it had a population of 60,000 free settlers.*

10. Many Americans saw Shays' Rebellion as *a sign that the Articles of Confederation did not work.*

B. Reviewing Key Terms
Directions: Complete each sentence by writing the correct term in the blank.

11. _____*Bill of Rights*_____ is a list of freedoms that the government promises to protect.

12. The _____*Articles of Confederation*_____ set up a loose alliance of the 13 states.

13. The _____*Land Ordinance of 1783*_____ set up rules for settling the Northwest Territory.

14. The _____*Northwest Ordinance*_____ set up a government for the Northwest Territory.

15. In an uprising known as _____*Shays' Rebellion*_____, farmers attacked the Massachusetts government for raising taxes.

CHAPTER

7

Section 2 Guided Reading and Review

The Constitutional Convention

A. As You Read

Directions: As you read Section 2 in your textbook, answer the following questions:

Possible answers below

1. What was the original goal of the Constitutional Convention? <u>to revise the Articles</u>

   <u>of Confederation</u>

2. Why is James Madison called "the Father of the Constitution"? <u>Madison was well</u>

   <u>prepared for the debates, and his ideas about a democratic government influenced his fellow delegates.</u>

3. Why did the delegates keep their debates secret? <u>They wanted to speak freely and also to</u>

   <u>avoid outside influences.</u>

4. How would the legislature differ under the Virginia Plan and the New Jersey Plan?

   <u>The Virginia Plan called for two houses with seats based on population; the New Jersey Plan called for one house</u>

   <u>with each state having one vote.</u>

5. What was Roger Sherman's main contribution to the Convention? <u>Sherman proposed</u>

   <u>the Great Compromise, which provided for a two-house legislature. In the upper house, each state would have two</u>

   <u>votes; in the lower house, the number of a state's representatives would be based on population.</u>

6. How was the dispute between states over the question of the slave population resolved?

   <u>The Three-Fifths Compromise stated that three fifths of the slave population of each state would be counted in</u>

   <u>the state's overall population.</u>

7. What were the Northern and Southern positions on outlawing the slave trade?

   <u>Northern states wanted the slave trade banned everywhere. Southern states did not want it banned because their</u>

   <u>economies depended on slave labor.</u>

8. How was this disagreement resolved? <u>Delegates agreed that Congress could not outlaw the slave</u>

   <u>trade for 20 years and that states could not stop a fugitive slave from being returned to an owner.</u>

9. How would the Constitution be approved and go into effect? <u>Each state was to hold a</u>

   <u>convention to approve or reject the Constitution. When nine states approved it, the Constitution would go into effect.</u>

B. Reviewing Key Terms

Directions: Briefly describe the responsibilities of each branch of government.

10. legislative branch <u>passes the laws</u>

11. executive branch <u>carries out the laws</u>

12. judicial branch <u>ensures that laws are carried out fairly</u>

CHAPTER

7

Section 3 Guided Reading and Review

Ideas Behind the Constitution

A. As You Read

Directions: As you read Section 3 in your textbook, fill in the graphic organizer with the ideas that influenced the Constitution of the United States.

The Roman Republic	The American Experience
1. citizens rule themselves through elected representatives	6. tradition of government charters
2. virtues of independence	7. memories of grievances against English king

Great Britain	The Enlightenment
3. monarch must obey laws	8. all people have natural rights
4. nobles have certain rights	9. government is an agreement between the ruler and the ruled
5. English Bill of Rights	10. separation of powers

B. Reviewing Key Terms

Directions: Define the following terms.

11. republic   government in which citizens rule themselves through elected representatives

12. dictatorship   government in which one person or a small group holds complete authority

13. Magna Carta   document signed by King John of England in 1215; stated that the monarch must obey the laws and that English nobles had certain rights

14. habeas corpus   no person can be held in prison without being charged with a specific crime

CHAPTER

7

Section 4 Guided Reading and Review

Ratification and the Bill of Rights

A. As You Read

Directions: Complete the crossword puzzle below as you read Section 4 in your textbook.

Across

1. To approve the Constitution *ratify*
4. Needed to protect basic liberties *Bill of Rights*
5. Amendment that protects freedom of religion, speech, and the press *first*
7. Assembly that proposed the first 10 amendments *Congress*

Down

2. Believed in a strong national government *Federalist*
3. Last state to approve the Constitution *Rhode Island*
6. What Antifederalists thought states would be *weak*

```
¹R A T I ²F Y
        E
        D
        E
        R       ³R
        A       H
   ⁴B I L L O F R I G H T S
        I       O
        S       D
                E
   ⁵F I R S T   I      ⁶W
                S      E
            ⁷C O N G R E S S
                L      A
                A      K
                N
                D
```

B. Reviewing Key Terms

Directions: Define the following terms.

8. *The Federalist Papers* essays written by Madison, Hamilton, and Jay to explain and defend the Constitution

9. amend *to change*

CHAPTER

8

Section 1 Guided Reading and Review

Goals and Principles of the Constitution

A. As You Read

Directions: As you read Section 1 in your textbook, complete the graphic organizer by writing in the goals and principles of the Constitution.

The Constitution

Goals

Answers for numbers 1–6 can be in any order.

1. to form a more perfect union

2. to establish justice

3. to ensure domestic tranquillity

4. to provide for the common defense

5. to promote the general welfare

6. to secure the blessing of liberty

Principles

Answers for numbers 7–13 can be in any order.

7. popular sovereignty

8. limited government

9. separation of powers

10. checks and balances

11. federalism

12. republicanism

13. individual rights

B. Reviewing Key Terms

Directions: Define the following terms.

14. Preamble   the opening statement of the Constitution _____

15. Articles   one of the sections of the Constitution _____

16. general welfare   the well-being of all the nation's citizens _____

Name _____ Class _____ Date _____

Section 2 Guided Reading and Review
How the Federal Government Works

A. As You Read

Directions: As you read Section 2 in your textbook, complete the chart below by listing key facts that describe each branch of government.

	Legislative	Executive	Judicial (Supreme Court)
Officer(s)	1. Speaker of the House 2. President of the Senate	8. President 9. Vice President	12. Justices
Primary Duty	3. make laws	10. carry out nation's laws	13. decide what Constitution means
Checks on other branches	4. override veto 5. approve presidential appointments 6. ratify treaties 7. impeach the President	11. veto bills	14. declare laws unconstitutional

B. Reviewing Key Terms

Directions: Define the following terms.

15. bill _proposal for a law_ _____

16. electoral college _system for electing a President_ _____

17. appeal _a request that a higher court review a lower court's decision_ _____

18. veto _rejection of a bill by the President_ _____

19. override _overruling a presidential veto_ _____

20. impeach _to bring charges of serious wrongdoing against the President or other elected official_ _____

Name _____ Class _____ Date _____

Section 3 Guided Reading and Review

Changing the Constitution

A. As You Read

Directions: As you read Section 3 in your textbook, answer the following questions:

1. Why did the framers provide for changes to the Constitution? They knew that the country
   would change and that the Constitution would have to change also.

2. What are the two ways in which an amendment to the Constitution can be ratified?
   The legislatures of three fourths of the states or special conventions in three fourths of the states can approve it.

3. What is the overall purpose of the Bill of Rights? It protects the basic rights of all citizens.

List the provisions of each of the 10 amendments in the Bill of Rights.

4. First: freedom of speech, of religion, and of the press; the right to peacefully assemble and petition the government

5. Second: the right to bear arms

6. Third: the government cannot force citizens to shelter troops in their homes

7. Fourth: protection from unlawful search of home or property

8. Fifth: people cannot be forced to give evidence against themselves

9. Sixth: right to a speedy and public trial by a fair jury

10. Seventh: right to a trial by jury in civil cases

11. Eighth: judges forbidden to impose unreasonable fines or punishments

12. Ninth: a citizen's rights are not limited to those specified in the Constitution

13. Tenth: all powers not given by the Constitution to the national government or denied to the states are reserved for the states or the people

B. Reviewing Key Terms

Directions: Explain what each of the following added to the Constitution.

14. Civil War Amendments abolished slavery, guaranteed citizenship to former slaves, and forbade states to
    deny any citizen the right to vote on the basis of race, color, or former slave status

15. Nineteenth Amendment
    gave women the right to vote

16. Twenty-sixth Amendment
    lowered the legal voting age from 21 to 18

CHAPTER

8

Section 4 Guided Reading and Review

State and Local Governments

A. As You Read

Directions: As you read Section 4 in your textbook, complete the graphic organizer by listing the powers and services of state and local governments.

State Governments	Local Governments
<u>Power determined by:</u>	<u>Power Determined by:</u>
1. Constitution	11. state
<u>Services</u>	<u>Services</u>
2. maintains law and order	12. runs the schools supervised by the state
3. enforces criminal law	13. provides firefighters, police, and garbage collectors
4. protects property	14. provides sewers and water
5. regulates business	15. maintains local roads and hospitals
6. supervises public education	16. inspects buildings and restaurants for safety
7. provides public health and welfare	
8. builds and maintains highways	
9. operates state parks and forests	
10. regulates the use of state-owned land	

B. Reviewing Key Terms

Directions: Define the following terms.

17. constitutional initiative process by which citizens propose an amendment to a state constitution; signatures gathered on a petition, which goes to legislature or citizens for approval

18. infrastructure system of roads, bridges, and tunnels

19. local government government on the county, parish, city, town, village, or district level

Name _____ Class _____ Date _____

Section 5 Guided Reading and Review

Rights and Responsibilities of Citizens

A. As You Read *Possible answers below*

Directions: As you read Section 5 in your textbook, answer the following questions:

1. In what two ways can a person be considered a citizen of the United States by birth?

   be born in the United States or have one parent who is a citizen of the United States when the person was born

2. How does an adult become a naturalized citizen? *A person must live legally for at least five years in the United States; submit an application; pass tests on American history, government, and the English language; show good moral character; and swear an oath of allegiance.*

3. What are some basic rights United States citizens enjoy? *freedom of speech, freedom of religion, freedom to own property, freedom to travel freely, the right to a fair trial*

List six basic responsibilities of a citizen, and give one reason for fulfilling each.
Possible answers below

4. *Voting: People should be informed in order to vote for candidates who will best represent the country.*

5. *Obeying the laws: Laws are made to protect all citizens, so citizens should obey them.*

6. *Defending the nation: Because the nation protects and defends its citizens, they must in turn protect the nation if it is attacked or invaded.*

7. *Serving on a jury: If people want the right to be tried by a jury, they must serve on juries when they are called.*

8. *Serving the community: A community helps and shelters those who live in it. In turn, citizens should work for their community.*

9. *Being informed: People cannot protect their rights unless they are informed about current events, the law, and government.*

B. Reviewing Key Terms

Directions: Complete the sentences in Column I with the terms in Column II. Write the letter of the correct answer in the space provided.

Column I

___d___ 10. A feeling of love and devotion toward one's country is called _____.

___b___ 11. A/An _____ is a person who enters another country in order to settle there.

___e___ 12. A/An _____ is a noncitizen living in the country.

___a___ 13. Every citizen has a responsibility to serve when called for _____.

___c___ 14. A/An _____ citizen is one who has completed the official legal process for becoming a citizen.

Column II

a. jury duty

b. immigrant

c. naturalized

d. patriotism

e. resident alien

CHAPTER

9 Section 1 Guided Reading and Review
Washington Takes Office

A. As You Read

Directions: As you read Section 1 in your textbook, answer the following questions.

1. What were the first five executive departments of the federal government? _____

   the departments of State, Treasury, and War, and the offices of Attorney General and Postmaster General

   _____

2. Who are members of the President's Cabinet, and what is their function? _____

   the heads of the executive departments, who serve as advisers to the President

3. What did the Judiciary Act establish? It set up the federal court system. It established the Supreme
   Court with one Chief Justice and five Associate Justices. It set up a system of district and circuit courts across
   the United States.

4. How did Hamilton propose to repay the national debt, and what was the response of

   the opposition? Hamilton wanted the government to buy all national and state bonds and issue new bonds

   to pay off the old debts. The opposition argued that this system would reward speculators.

5. What steps did the government take to strengthen the economy? _____

   The government established a national bank, issued paper money, made loans, and placed tariffs on foreign goods.

6. What was the purpose of the tax on whiskey? to raise money for the Treasury

   _____

7. Who rebelled during the Whiskey Rebellion, and what was the outcome? _____
   Farmers who made whiskey from their corn crops protested the tax. The government sent troops against the rebels,
   who returned to their farms.

B. Reviewing Key People

Directions: Match each description in Column I with the correct name in Column II.
Write the letter of the answer in the space provided.

Column I

_c_ 8. first President of the United States; served
   two terms

_e_ 9. first Secretary of State

_b_ 10. first Secretary of the Treasury; set up the
   Bank of the United States

_d_ 11. led the opposition to the government's plan
   for repaying the national debt

_a_ 12. first Chief Justice of the Supreme Court

Column II

a. John Jay

b. Alexander Hamilton

c. George Washington

d. James Madison

e. Thomas Jefferson

Guided Reading and Review

CHAPTER

9

Section 2 Guided Reading and Review

Creating a Foreign Policy

A. As You Read

Directions: As you read Section 2 in your textbook, complete the following sentences.
Possible answers below

1. American responses to the French Revolution were divided. Americans supported the French people's desire for liberty, but they were horrified by the violence of the Reign of Terror.

2. Washington's Cabinet members had the following opinions on the French Revolution: Jefferson supported the French people; he believed they had the right to use violence to win their freedom. Hamilton and Adams believed that violence was no way to create democracy.

3. The main foreign policy issue facing President Washington was how to remain neutral in European wars while honoring agreements to support France.

4. The Neutrality Proclamation stated that The United States would not support Britain or France in their war.

5. Jay's Treaty provided that Britain would pay damages for American ships it had seized, and it would give up its forts in the West. The United States would pay old debts to British merchants.

6. In his Farewell Address, George Washington advised the nation not to become involved in European affairs.

B. Reviewing Key Terms

Directions: Define the following terms.

7. French Revolution successful uprising of the French people against the monarchy

8. foreign policy actions that a nation takes in relation to other nations

9. neutral not taking sides in a war

10. Farewell Address speech given by President Washington just before he left office

CHAPTER

9

Section 3 Guided Reading and Review
Political Parties Emerge

A. As You Read

Directions: Complete the chart below as you read Section 3 in your textbook. Fill in details about the differences between the Federalists and the Democratic Republicans.

	Federalists	**Democratic Republicans**
Basis of economy	1. manufacturing and trade	5. farming
Federal or state powers	2. The federal government has more power than state governments.	6. federal government as small as possible
Interpretation of the Constitution	3. loose	7. strict
Foreign policy	4. pro-British	8. pro-French

B. Reviewing Key People

Directions: Briefly identify the following people. Mark Federalists with an *F* and Democratic Republicans with a *DR*.

__F__ 9. Alexander Hamilton leader of the Federalist party and Washington's Secretary of the Treasury

__DR__ 10. Thomas Jefferson leader of the Democratic Republican party; Washington's Secretary of State

__DR__ 11. George Clinton Governor of New York

__DR__ 12. Aaron Burr leading New York politician

__F__ 13. John Fenno publisher of the *Gazette of the United States*

__DR__ 14. Philip Freneau publisher of the *National Gazette*

CHAPTER

9

Section 4 Guided Reading and Review

The Second President

A. As You Read

Directions: As you read Section 4 in your textbook, fill in supporting details for each of the main ideas listed below. *Possible answers below*

Main Idea A: As President Adams took office, the United States faced a crisis with France.

1. The French objected to Jay's Treaty because it favored Britain.

2. France began seizing American ships.

3. The XYZ Affair outraged Americans who saw the demand for money as asking for a bribe.

Main Idea B: The Federalist Party split during the Adams administration.

4. Led by Hamilton, many Federalists favored war with France.

5. Led by Adams, others wanted peace.

Main Idea C: The Alien and Sedition acts raised the issue of states' rights.

6. The Alien Act allowed the President to deport any foreigner thought to be dangerous to the country and extended the wait for citizenship from 5 to 14 years.

7. The Sedition Act stated that citizens could be fined or jailed for criticizing the government.

8. Kentucky and Virginia passed resolutions claiming that states could nullify federal laws.

B. Reviewing Key Terms

Directions: Complete each sentence below by writing the correct term in the blank.

9. The _____XYZ Affair_____ involved discussions between French agents and American diplomats.

10. President Adams did not want war, but he strengthened the navy by building _____frigates_____.

11. _____Sedition_____ is the act of stirring up rebellion against a government.

12. Kentucky and Virginia wanted to be able to _____nullify_____ federal laws.

13. The _____Kentucky and Virginia resolutions_____ claimed that each state had the power to judge whether a law was unconstitutional.

CHAPTER 10

Section 1 Guided Reading and Review

A Republican Takes Office

A. As You Read

Directions: As you read Section 1, answer the following questions. *Possible answers below*

1. Why did Thomas Jefferson want to make the government more democratic?

   Jefferson believed that the nation's strength came from ordinary people. He thought that citizens should be

   educated in order to participate in democracy and preserve liberty.

2. How did Federalists feel about Jefferson's election?

   Federalists feared that Jefferson might bring revolutionary changes to the nation because he supported the French

   revolution. They also thought he might punish them for putting Republicans in jail under the Alien and Sedition acts.

3. What goals did Jefferson achieve in reducing the size of government?

   Jefferson cut the federal budget, reduced government spending and debt, supported the idea of little government

   regulation in economic activities, decreased the size of government departments, reduced the size of the military,

   and asked Congress to repeal the whiskey tax.

4. What action did Jefferson take when the Sedition Act expired?

   Jefferson pardoned people who were in jail because of the act, and he asked Congress to restore the law allowing

   foreign-born people to become citizens after five years.

5. What was the major difference in the philosophies of Jefferson and John Marshall?

   Marshall was a Federalist who, unlike Jefferson, believed in a strong central government.

6. What was the outcome of *Marbury* v. *Madison*?

   The case was decided in Madison's favor because the Court said the Judiciary Act was unconstitutional. This

   decision established the Supreme Court's power to decide whether laws passed by Congress are unconstitutional.

B. Reviewing Key Terms

Directions: Match the definitions in Column I with the terms in Column II.

Column I

___c___ 7. idea that government should play as small a role as possible in economic affairs

___a___ 8. an economy with little regulation

___b___ 9. Supreme Court decides whether laws are constitutional

Column II

a. free market

b. judicial review

c. laissez faire

Name _____ Class _____ Date _____

Section 2 Guided Reading and Review
The Louisiana Purchase

A. As You Read
Directions: As you read Section 2, complete the following sentences. *Possible answers below*

1. Settlers west of the Appalachians relied on the Mississippi River for

   shipping their goods through New Orleans to ports on the Atlantic coast.

2. The United States wanted to purchase New Orleans and West Florida because

   Jefferson did not want France to gain an empire in North America, and he wanted control of the port of New Orleans.

3. The French offered to sell all of Louisiana because

   France needed money to pay for its European wars.

4. Jefferson sent Lewis and Clark to explore the Louisiana territory because

   Americans knew nothing about the land, Jefferson wanted them to map a route to the Pacific Ocean, and good

   relationships with the Indians could lead to trade with them.

5. Sacagawea's contribution to the Lewis and Clark expedition was

   her knowledge of medicinal herbs and her presence, which was a sign of friendliness.

6. The expedition had peaceful dealings with the Indians because

   they were traveling with an Indian woman and her baby, which suggested that they were friendly.

7. Zebulon Pike explored

   the upper Mississippi River, the Arkansas River, and parts of present-day Colorado and New Mexico.

B. Reviewing Key Terms
Directions: Define each of the following terms.

8. Pinckney Treaty *agreement between Spain and the United States that allowed Americans to ship goods down*

   the Mississippi River and store them in New Orleans

9. Louisiana Purchase *1803 American purchase of Louisiana from France; doubled the size of the United States*

10. continental divide *a mountain ridge that separates river systems, causing them to flow toward opposite*

    sides of a continent

CHAPTER

10 Section 3 Guided Reading and Review
New Threats From Overseas

A. As You Read

Directions: As you read Section 3, complete the chart below by writing supporting details under each main idea. *Possible answers below*

Main Idea A: After the Revolution, American overseas trade grew rapidly.

1. Traders from New England traded ice for silk and spices from India.

2. New England merchants built up a thriving trade with China.

3. New Englanders sailed up the Pacific coast and traded for furs, which they sold in China.

4. American traders operating in the Mediterranean Sea paid the rulers of the Barbary States to prevent pirate attacks.

Main Idea B: Britain and France violated American neutrality.

5. France seized American ships on their way to England.

6. The British captured American ships on their way to France and forced American sailors into service in the British navy.

Main Idea C: Jefferson hoped that an American embargo would hurt Britain and France.

7. The Embargo Act cut off all foreign trade.

8. American merchants were unable to import or export goods.

9. Because the Embargo Act was too strict, it was replaced by an act banning trade with only Britain and France.

B. Reviewing Key Terms

Directions: Complete each sentence by writing the correct term in the blank.

10. To protect its ships from attack, the United States paid a _____tribute_____ to Tripoli.

11. British _____impressment_____ gangs kidnapped young men and forced them into service in the British navy.

12. A law banning trade is called an _____embargo_____.

13. From 1807 to 1809, many American merchants violated trade laws by _____smuggling_____.

CHAPTER

10 Section 4 Guided Reading and Review

The Road to War

A. As You Read

Directions: As you read Section 4, fill in the graphic organizer with the reasons why the United States and Britain went to war.

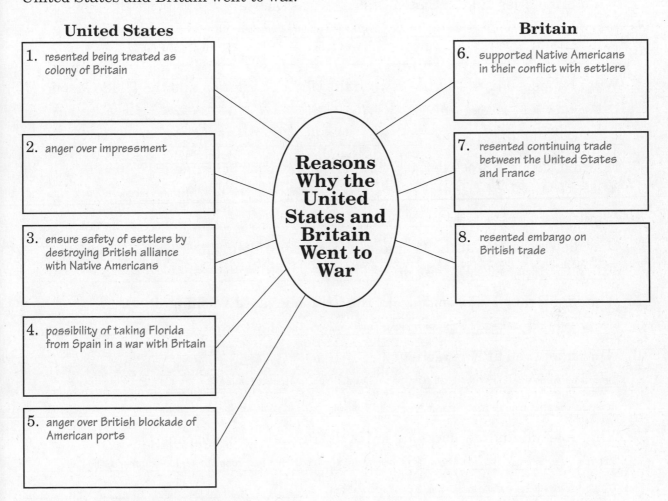

United States

1. resented being treated as colony of Britain

2. anger over impressment

3. ensure safety of settlers by destroying British alliance with Native Americans

4. possibility of taking Florida from Spain in a war with Britain

5. anger over British blockade of American ports

Reasons Why the United States and Britain Went to War

Britain

6. supported Native Americans in their conflict with settlers

7. resented continuing trade between the United States and France

8. resented embargo on British trade

B. Reviewing Key Terms

Directions: Identify each person listed below, and describe his role in the conflict between white settlers and Native Americans.

9. Tecumseh _leader of the Shawnees who organized Indian nations into a confederation to fight for their lands_

_____

10. Tenskwatawa "The Prophet" _Shawnee leader, and brother of Tecumseh, who led Native American forces_

in the Battle of Tippecanoe

11. William Henry Harrison _governor of Indiana territory who led American forces at the Battle of_

Tippecanoe, defeating the Indians

Name _____ Class _____ Date _____

Section 5 Guided Reading and Review
The War of 1812

A. As You Read

Directions: As you read Section 5, answer the following questions. *Possible answers below*

1. What difficulties did the United States face as the War of 1812 began?

   small and poorly equipped army; small navy; poorly trained volunteer soldiers

2. What happened in the battle between the USS *Constitution* and the HMS *Guerrière*?

   The *Constitution* fired on the *Guerrière* and caused enough damage to force the *Guerrière's* captain to surrender.

3. How did General Brock defeat the American invasion of Canada?

   He dressed his soldiers in red coats to make them look like British troops; he led Americans to believe that Native

   Americans were helping the Canadian soldiers.

4. How did the battles at the Thames and Horseshoe Bend affect Native Americans?
   Tecumseh died in the Battle of the Thames, and the Indian confederation fell apart. After the Americans won the
   Battle of Horseshoe Bend, the Indians surrendered.

5. What did Dolley Madison do when the British invaded Washington, D.C.?

   She fled the White House with important papers and George Washington's portrait.

6. What happened at Fort McHenry?

   The British bombarded the harbor all night but withdrew in the morning because the fort held. Francis Scott Key

   observed the battle and wrote a poem, "The Star-Spangled Banner," that would later become the national anthem.

7. What role did Andrew Jackson play in the Battle of New Orleans?

   Jackson led experienced troops who dug trenches from which to fight. The troops under his command killed

   2,000 British soldiers while losing only 7 of their own men.

8. What did the United States and Britain agree to after the war ended?
   They agreed to restore prewar conditions.

B. Reviewing Key Terms

Directions: Identify the significance of the following terms.

9. Battle of Lake Erie It was a victory for the Americans.

10. Battle of New Orleans It was a victory for the Americans; Andrew Jackson became a national hero.
                           New Englanders who opposed the war threatened to leave the Union if it continued;
11. Hartford Convention the convention broke up as soon as the war ended.

12. Treaty of Ghent It was the peace treaty that ended the War of 1812 and restored prewar conditions.

CHAPTER 11

Section 1 Guided Reading and Review

The Industrial Revolution

A. As You Read

Directions: As you read Section 1 in your textbook, write one cause and one effect for each of the following events. *Possible answers below*

1. The Industrial Revolution began in Britain in the mid-1700s.

    Cause: British inventors developed new machines that speeded up the manufacturing process.

    Effect: The Industrial Revolution spread to the United States.

2. Samuel Slater memorized the design of the machines in British textile mills.

    Cause: It was illegal to take plans for the machines out of England.

    Effect: Slater soon built the first successful water-powered textile mill in the United States.

3. Eli Whitney invented machines that could manufacture identical parts.

    Cause: Whitney wanted to speed up the manufacturing process.

    Effect: Inventors soon designed machines to produce interchangeable parts for many other goods.

4. Francis Cabot Lowell's partners built a factory town named for him.

    Cause: Lowell combined spinning and weaving operations under one roof.

    Effect: Lowell became a model factory town; the population grew to more than 10,000 people.

5. Textile mills hired young women.

    Cause: Mill owners could pay lower wages to women than to men.

    Effect: Many young women left home and became economically independent or used their wages to help their families.

B. Reviewing Key Terms

Directions: Define the following terms.

6. spinning jenny machine that could spin several threads at once

7. capitalist person who invests in a business in order to make a profit

8. factory system system that brought workers and machines together under one roof to produce goods

9. urbanization movement of the population from farms to the cities

CHAPTER

11  Section 2 Guided Reading and Review

Americans Move Westward

A. As You Read

Directions: As you read Section 2 in your textbook, fill in the supporting details for each main idea. *Possible answers below*

Main Idea A: Many settlers traveled westward during the early 1800s.

1. _New roads such as the Great Wagon Road made it easier for settlers to travel west._

2. _As more and more people traveled west, more territories applied for statehood._

3. _Private companies began paving roads and collecting tolls that paid for road maintenance._

4. _Congress approved money to build the National Road._

Main Idea B: In the early 1800s, Americans found faster and better ways to travel or move goods by water.

5. _The invention of the steam engine and the steamboat made passenger and cargo travel much faster._

6. _Steamboats made it much cheaper for western farmers to ship goods._

7. _The Erie Canal linked the Great Lakes with the Mohawk and Hudson rivers and made it possible to ship goods directly to New York._

B. Reviewing Key Terms

Directions: Match the terms in Column I with the definitions in Column II. Write the letter of the correct answer in the space provided.

Column I

___b___ 8. turnpike

___a___ 9. corduroy road

___d___ 10. *Clermont*

___c___ 11. Erie Canal

Column II

a. road paved with logs

b. road on which tolls were collected

c. linked the Great Lakes with the Mohawk and Hudson rivers

d. began the age of steamboats

Name _____ Class _____ Date _____

11 Section 3 Guided Reading and Review
Unity and Division

A. As You Read

Directions: Complete the chart below as you read Section 3 in your textbook. Fill in information to compare and contrast the ideas and political positions of three sectional leaders. *Possible answers below*

John C. Calhoun (South)	Daniel Webster (North)	Henry Clay (West)
1. supported War of 1812	4. opposed War of 1812	7. supported War of 1812
2. supported slavery	5. supported strong federal government	8. supported strong federal government
3. opposed strong federal government	6. opposed slavery	9. supported protective tariff

B. Reviewing Key Terms

Directions: Briefly define or identify each term.

10. Era of Good Feelings period of national pride after victory in War of 1812

11. sectionalism loyalty to one's state or section rather than to the nation as a whole

12. American System program proposed by Clay, calling for high tariffs on imports, which would help northern factories

13. internal improvements improvements for bridges, roads, and canals

14. *McCulloch* v. *Maryland* Supreme Court decision that determined that states had no right to interfere with federal institutions within their borders

15. *Gibbons* v. *Ogden* Supreme Court decision upholding the power of the federal government to regulate commerce

16. interstate commerce trade between individual states

CHAPTER

11

Section 4 Guided Reading and Review

New Nations in the Americas

A. As You Read

Directions: Complete the following sentences as you read Section 4 in your textbook.
Possible answers below

1. Latin American nations were eager for independence because their people had little or no say in government; Spain's policies toward native Latin Americans were harsh.

2. Mexico gained its independence when creoles joined the revolutionary movement.

3. The United Provinces of Central America included the present-day nations of Nicaragua, Costa Rica, El Salvador, Honduras, and Guatemala.

4. Latin American republics did not unite as a single country because they covered a huge area, and geographic features such as mountain ranges made travel and communication difficult.

5. Spain gave up its rights to Florida in exchange for $5 million.

6. The Monroe Doctrine stated that the United States would not interfere in the affairs of European nations or their colonies, and it warned European nations not to try to regain control of newly independent Latin American nations.

B. Reviewing Key People

Directions: Explain the role that each of the following people played in achieving Latin American independence. Possible answers below

7. Miguel Hidalgo called for all Mexicans, including Indians, to join in the struggle for independence

8. José Morelos leader in Mexican Revolution; called for a program giving land to peasants

9. Simón Bolívar led Venezuela to independence; became president of Republic of Grand Colombia

10. José de San Martín led Argentina to independence; played leadership role in revolutions in Chile, Peru, and Ecuador

11. Prince Pedro of Portugal agreed to Brazil's demand for independence; became the first emperor of independent Brazil

Name _____ Class _____ Date _____

Section 1 Guided Reading and Review

A New Era in Politics

A. As You Read

Directions: As you read Section 1 in your textbook, fill in the chart to compare and contrast John Quincy Adams and Andrew Jackson.

	John Quincy Adams	**Andrew Jackson**
1. home state	Massachusetts	Tennessee
2. family background	son of former President, family of professionals and political leaders	born in a log cabin to farmers
3. professional background	former Secretary of State	military leader in War of 1812
4. political party	Republican, later a Whig	Republican, later a Democrat
5. political philosophy	believed in strong central government, called for federal support of arts, sciences, and transportation	supported working people and small farmers

B. Reviewing Key Terms

Directions: Define each term.

6. suffrage the right to vote

7. majority more than half

8. Whig political party that supported strong federal government; formerly called National Republicans

9. Democrat political party that supported Andrew Jackson; included farmers and factory workers

10. caucus private meeting in which candidates are chosen

11. nominating convention meeting in which delegates of all states choose the party's candidate for President

Name _____ Class _____ Date _____

CHAPTER

12 Section 2 Guided Reading and Review

Jackson in the White House

A. As You Read

Directions: As you read Section 2 in your textbook, answer the following questions.

1. What was Andrew Jackson's early professional experience? He was a lawyer and landowner;
later he was elected to Congress. He led troops in the War of 1812.

2. How did President Jackson plan to reform the government? by appointing many ordinary
citizens (his own supporters) to government posts

3. Why did Jackson oppose the existence of the National Bank? He thought it was
undemocratic and too powerful.

4. What powers did the National Bank have? It controlled loans made by state banks; it could limit
the amount these banks could lend.

5. How did Clay and Webster try to save the National Bank? They persuaded the president
of the Bank to apply early for renewal of the charter so that it would be an issue in the 1832 election. They believed
that if Jackson blocked the renewal, he would lose the election.

6. How did Jackson eventually destroy the National Bank? He vetoed its request for charter
renewal. After he won the election, he stopped depositing federal money in the bank. It closed in 1836.

B. Reviewing Key Terms

Directions: Use each term correctly in a sentence about the Jackson administration.
Possible answers below

7. spoils system Because the spoils belong to the winner of a contest, Jackson's practice of rewarding his
supporters with government jobs became known as the spoils system.

8. kitchen cabinet Jackson's kitchen cabinet was an informal group of advisers who met in the White House kitchen.

CHAPTER

12 Section 3 Guided Reading and Review

A New Crisis

A. As You Read

Directions: Complete the following sentences as you read Section 3 in your textbook.

1. Southerners hated the 1828 tariff because it raised the prices on the goods they imported; they thought it was unconstitutional.

2. Daniel Webster argued against nullification on the grounds that if states had the right to cancel federal laws, the nation would fall apart.

3. The Indian Removal Act forced Indians to move west of the Mississippi River to barren lands.

4. Causes of the Panic of 1837 included loans state banks made to land speculators, the printing by state banks of paper money not backed by gold or silver, the closing of banks, and the lowering of cotton prices because of a surplus crop.

5. To ease the economic depression, President Van Buren tried to stabilize the banking system and cut back on federal expenses.

6. Changes in political campaigns that started in 1840 included candidates' traveling and giving speeches, rallies, banquets, entertainment, and mudslinging.

B. Reviewing Key Terms

Directions: Match each term in Column I with the correct definition in Column II. Write the letter of the correct answer in the space provided.

Column I

__c__ 7. nullification

__a__ 8. depression

__b__ 9. mudslinging

Column II

a. a period in which business declines and many people lose their jobs

b. the use of insults to attack an opponent's reputation

c. cancellation

CHAPTER 13

Section 1 Guided Reading and Review

Oregon Country

A. As You Read

Directions: As you read Section 1 in your textbook, write details about Oregon Country in the following chart. *Possible answers below*

	Oregon Country
Land	1. fertile soil along Pacific coast
	2. inland mountain range with dense forests
	3. barren, dry plateau between coastal mountains and Rocky Mountains
Climate	4. mild temperatures
	5. plentiful rainfall
Journey to Oregon	6. Wagon trains formed at Independence, Missouri, in spring to reach Oregon by October.
	7. People camped along the way.
	8. Dangers of travel included drowning, heat, early snowstorms, and illnesses.
Who Traveled There	9. fur traders
	10. trappers or "mountain men"
	11. missionaries
	12. families intending to farm the land
Occupations in Oregon	13. fur trading
	14. farming
	15. missionaries

B. Reviewing Key People

Directions: Briefly identify each of the following people.

16. **Jedediah Smith** mountain man who led settlers across the Rockies through South Pass

17. **Manuel Lisa** Latino fur trader who led a trip up the Missouri River and founded Fort Manuel

18. **James Beckwourth** African American who became a chief of the Crow Indians and discovered a route to California through the Sierra Nevada

19. **Marcus and Narcissa Whitman** missionaries to Native Americans in Oregon

Name _____ Class _____ Date _____

Section 2 Guided Reading and Review
The Republic of Texas

A. As You Read

Directions: Use the letters A through E to put the following events into chronological order as you read Section 2 in your textbook. Write the letter in the space provided. Then, write a sentence about the importance of each event.

___D___ 1. The Mexican army began the siege of the Alamo.

Because nearly all the Texans died or were executed, outrage made many more Texans and Americans join

the struggle against Mexico.

___B___ 2. Mexico barred any more Americans from settling in Texas.

American settlers in Texas felt resentment and anger that fueled the conflict.

___E___ 3. Sam Houston led his troops to victory at the Battle of San Jacinto.

This Texan victory forced Santa Anna to agree to grant Texas its independence.

___C___ 4. The Republic of Texas declared its independence from Mexico.

This action led to a war in which Mexico tried to retake Texas.

___A___ 5. Spain gave American Moses Austin permission to establish a colony in Texas.

This colony marked the beginning of the involvement of the United States in Texas.

B. Reviewing Key People and Terms

Directions: Complete the following sentences by writing the correct person or term in the space provided.

6. Mexicans who lived in Texas were called _____Tejanos_____.

7. During the _____siege_____ no food or water could reach the Texans defending the Alamo.

8. The _____Battle of San Jacinto_____ resulted in the capture of General Santa Anna.

9. Texas was called the _____Lone Star_____ Republic because of the design on its flag.

10. _____Sam Houston_____ became the first president of the Republic of Texas.

Name _____ Class _____ Date _____

CHAPTER

13 Section 3 Guided Reading and Review

California and the Southwest

A. As You Read

Directions: Below are three main ideas from Section 3 in your textbook. As you read, fill in the supporting details for each main idea.   *Possible answers below*

Main Idea A: New Mexico Territory was home to three cultures.

1. Native Americans lived by farming or hunting.

2. Spain claimed the region and established Santa Fe as the capital.

3. Americans settled there after Mexico became independent.

Main Idea B: Settlements in California included missions and ranches.

4. Spanish missionaries built the first European settlements in California.

5. Native Americans herded and farmed for the missionaries.

6. Mexico gave away mission lands to the wealthy for cattle ranches.

7. Native American and Mexican ranch workers developed the culture of the vaqueros.

Main Idea C: Many Americans supported the idea of western expansion.

8. Some officials wanted to control California's ports of San Francisco and San Diego.

9. Americans believed in Manifest Destiny, the idea that the United States had a right to spread American culture to the Pacific Ocean.

10. Americans showed support for expansion by electing James Polk President.

B. Reviewing Key Terms

Directions: Briefly explain the relevance of each term to the westward expansion of the United States.

11. **New Mexico Territory** huge region in the southwest; Americans settled there after Mexico gained its independence

12. **Santa Fe Trail** route from Missouri to Santa Fe, New Mexico, taken by many who went west

13. **Manifest Destiny** belief that the United States had a right to control all the land to the Pacific Ocean

Guided Reading and Review

CHAPTER

13 Section 4 Guided Reading and Review

The Mexican War

A. As You Read

Directions: Write in the missing cause or effect as you read Section 4 in your textbook.

1. Cause: President Polk did not want to fight Britain for control of Oregon.	1. Effect: The United States and Britain agreed to divide Oregon at latitude 49°N.
2. Cause: Sam Houston pretended that Texas might ally itself with Britain.	2. Effect: Congress admitted Texas to the Union.
3. Cause: Mexico refused to sell California and New Mexico to the United States.	3. Effect: War broke out between the United States and Mexico.
4. Cause: Mexican and American troops clashed in a disputed area of Texas.	4. Effect: Congress declared war on Mexico.
5. Cause: By 1847, the United States controlled New Mexico, California, and Mexico City.	5. Effect: The Mexican government moved to make peace.
6. Cause: The United States needed a strip of Mexican land to complete a railroad.	6. Effect: The United States bought the land from Mexico for $10 million.

B. Reviewing Key Terms

Directions: Match each term in Column I with the correct description in Column II. Write the letter of the correct answer in the space provided.

Column I

_c_ 7. Bear Flag Republic

_b_ 8. Treaty of Guadalupe-Hidalgo

_d_ 9. Mexican Cession

_a_ 10. Gadsden Purchase

Column II

a. land in present-day Arizona and New Mexico that Mexico sold to the United States for $10 million

b. stated that Mexico would cede California and New Mexico to the United States for $15 million

c. nickname given to California

d. lands Mexico sold to the United States at the end of the war

CHAPTER
13 Section 5 Guided Reading and Review
Americans Rush West

A. As You Read

Directions: As you read Section 5 in your textbook, answer the following questions.
Possible answers below

1. Why did Joseph Smith and his followers move west? People in settled areas opposed Mormon

   practices of polygamy and communal ownership of property; Mormons had to move west to be safe from persecution.

2. Why did many Americans go to California? They were looking for gold.

3. Why were the people who joined the gold rush called "forty-niners"? Gold was discovered

   in California in 1849.

4. How did a miner get gold from the earth? The miner dug it from the earth with knives, or scooped

   up sand and gravel from a riverbed and swirled it in the water, looking for gold among the pebbles.

5. What effect did the gold rush have on California? Cities became bigger. The population exploded.

   Crime increased. People came from all over the United States and the world. Most miners settled permanently in the

   area after the gold rush died down.

6. What did the gold rush mean for Mexican Americans and Indians? Many lost their land

   or were driven from it. Many Native Americans died of starvation or disease.

B. Reviewing Key Places

Directions: Briefly explain the importance of the following places to westward expansion or the gold rush.

7. Salt Lake City city the Mormons built near Utah's Great Salt Lake

8. Sutter's Mill place in California where gold was first discovered

9. San Francisco California town that became a major city during the gold rush

Name _____ Class _____ Date _____

CHAPTER

14 Section 1 Guided Reading and Review

Industry in the North

A. As You Read

Directions: As you read Section 1 in your textbook, answer the following questions.

Possible answers below

1. What could a sewing machine do that a tailor could not? It enabled workers to make many more items of clothing in much less time.

2. How was John Deere's plow an improvement over earlier plows? It was much lighter and could be pulled through a field more quickly.

3. What effect did Morse's telegraph have on American businesses? Merchants had faster access to information about supply, demand, and prices all over the country.

4. What were some of the problems with the first railroads? Soft roadbeds and weak bridges led to accidents. Locomotives often broke down. Hot embers from locomotives' smokestacks burned clothing or started fires.

5. Why were clipper ships able to sail faster than other types of ships? Clipper ships had tall masts and huge sails to catch wind. Their narrow hulls traveled quickly through water.

6. What effects did factories, new machines, and railroads have on the northern economy in the mid-1800s? Factories used steam power, so they could be built anywhere. Machines produced cheaper goods, so people bought more manufactured goods. Railroads provided fast, cheap transportation of raw materials and finished goods; opened new markets; and forced farmers into factory work because of cheap food prices.

B. Reviewing Key Terms

Directions: Briefly explain the function of the following inventions.

7. reaper machine that mowed grain

8. thresher machine that separated grain from its husks

9. telegraph device that sent electrical signals along wires; a code was used to send messages instantly

10. locomotive steam-powered engine that pulled rail cars along tracks

11. clipper ship fast-moving, narrow-hulled sailing ship

Guided Reading and Review

CHAPTER

14

Section 2 Guided Reading and Review
Life in the North

A. As You Read

Directions: Below are three main ideas from Section 2 in your textbook. As you read, fill in the supporting details for each main idea.   *Possible answers below*

Main Idea A: Factory conditions in the North grew worse as the century advanced.

1. *Laborers worked longer hours for less pay.*

2. *Factory machines were often dangerous, and accidents were common.*

Main Idea B: Workers began organizing to improve conditions.

3. *Trade unions began forming during the 1820s for the protection of the workers.*

4. *Workers won the right to a 10-hour day and the right to strike.*

Main Idea C: Immigrants faced both opportunity and hardship in the United States in the 1840s.

5. *Immigrants could earn higher wages in the United States.*

6. *Most of the jobs available to immigrants were low-paying factory jobs.*

7. *Immigrants with enough money were able to buy land.*

B. Reviewing Key Terms

Directions: Match each term in Column I with its definition in Column II. Write the letter of the correct answer in the space provided.

Column I

_f_ 8. artisan

_d_ 9. trade union

_b_ 10. strike

_a_ 11. famine

_c_ 12. nativist

_e_ 13. discrimination

Column II

a. severe food shortage

b. workers' refusal to do their jobs

c. one who wants to limit immigration and immigrants' rights

d. organized group of skilled workers who do the same types of jobs

e. policy or attitude that denies equal rights

f. skilled worker

CHAPTER

14

Section 3 Guided Reading and Review

Cotton Kingdom in the South

A. As You Read

Directions: Write in the missing cause or effect as you read Section 4 in your textbook.

1. Cause: Eli Whitney invented a machine that could separate cotton seeds from fibers.	1. Effect: The cotton gin could do the work of 50 people; cotton could now be grown at a huge profit.
2. Cause: Planters needed new land and began to move west.	2. Effect: Slavery spread further throughout the South.
3. Cause: Conditions for growing cotton were limited to certain areas of the South.	3. Effect: In other areas southerners raised rice, sugar cane, tobacco, and livestock.
4. Cause: Rich planters invested in land and slaves.	4. Effect: Southern industry remained small-scale.
5. Cause: The South depended on the North for almost all of its manufactured goods.	5. Effect: Southerners resented this dependency on the North.

B. Reviewing Key Terms

Directions: Define or identify each term.

6. cotton gin machine that separated cotton seeds from cotton fibers

7. Cotton Kingdom area in which cotton was the major crop, from South Carolina to Texas

CHAPTER

14 Section 4 Guided Reading and Review

Life in the South

A. As You Read

Directions: As you read Section 4 in your textbook, complete the following sentences.
Possible answers below

1. Planters dominated southern society because they had wealth and influence, and many became political leaders.

2. Slave owners created difficulties for free African Americans because they thought free African Americans would encourage slaves to rebel.

3. Rights that were denied to slaves included gathering in groups, leaving owner's property without a pass, owning guns, learning to read and write, voting, testifying in court, living and working where they chose, and being paid for their labor.

4. African American families were often separated because southern laws did not recognize slave marriages, and owners could sell family members to different buyers.

5. Christianity contributed to African American culture by offering hope and inspiring a new kind of religious song called a spiritual.

6. Slave revolts during the 1830s resulted in the deaths of whites and African Americans and the executions of the rebels.

B. Reviewing Key People and Terms

Directions: Define or identify the following people and terms.

7. cottonocracy wealthy families who raised cotton and owned many slaves

8. Denmark Vesey free African American who was betrayed and killed before his planned revolt began

9. slave codes state laws designed to prevent slaves from running away or rebelling

10. Nat Turner slave who led a rebellion and who was captured and hanged

Name _____ Class _____ Date _____

15 Section 1 Guided Reading and Review

The Reforming Spirit

A. As You Read

Directions: As you read Section 1 in your textbook, fill in the chart below by writing in details of each reform movement. *Possible answers below*

hospital reform	1. Dorothea Dix found that mentally ill people were locked up, abused, and treated as criminals rather than as patients.
	2. Legislation was passed so that the mentally ill were treated as patients rather than as criminals.
prison reform	3. Dorothea Dix and others investigated prisons and found crowded conditions and cold, damp cells where prisoners had to purchase food from jailers.
	4. Reforms improved prison buildings, banned cruel punishment, established shorter sentences, and stopped the treatment of debtors like criminals.
temperance movement	5. Women led the campaign against alcohol abuse because it led to abuse of families.
	6. Several states passed laws banning the sale of alcohol.
education reform	7. Few American children attended school, and teachers were poorly trained and poorly paid.
	8. States began passing laws requiring local governments to set up tax-supported schools, raise teachers' pay, and open colleges to train teachers.
	9. The first American schools for the blind and deaf opened in the early 1800s.

B. Reviewing Key Terms

Directions: Complete the following sentences by writing the correct term in the space provided.

10. In the mid-1800s, people became involved in _____social reform_____ to improve unjust or imperfect conditions in society.

11. Many Protestants believed in ___predestination___, which held that God decided in advance which people would attain salvation after death.

12. A huge outdoor meeting intended to stir up or renew religious feeling is called a _____revival_____.

CHAPTER 15

Section 2 Guided Reading and Review

Opposing Slavery

A. As You Read

Directions: Write in the missing cause or effect as you read Section 2 in your textbook.

1. Cause: In the 1800s, many Americans worked to end slavery.	→	**1. Effect:** By 1804, all states from Pennsylvania to New England had agreed to free their slaves.
2. Cause: The American Colonization Society founded Liberia as a colony for freed slaves.	→	**2. Effect:** A few thousand African Americans moved to Liberia.
3. Cause: Abolitionists formed the Underground Railroad.	→	**3. Effect:** Hundreds of slaves were able to escape to freedom in the North.
4. Cause: Harriet Tubman led over 300 slaves to freedom on the Underground Railroad.	→	**4. Effect:** Slave owners offered a $40,000 reward for the capture of Harriet Tubman.
5. Cause: Northern factories depended on southern cotton, and northern workers feared that freed slaves would take their jobs for lower wages.	→	**5. Effect:** Some northern manufacturers and workers opposed abolition.

B. Reviewing Key People

Directions: Briefly explain each person's contribution to the abolitionist movement.

6. Samuel Cornish established the abolitionist newspaper *Freedom's Journal* with John Russworm

7. Maria Stewart first American woman to make public speeches; spoke against slavery

8. Frederick Douglass escaped slave who exposed the cruelty of slavery in an autobiography and in public lectures

9. William Lloyd Garrison owner of *The Liberator*, an influential abolitionist newspaper; helped found the New England Antislavery Society

10. the Grimké sisters daughters of a slaveholder; worked for the abolition of slavery

11. Harriet Tubman escaped slave who led hundreds to freedom along the Underground Railroad

CHAPTER

15 Section 3 Guided Reading and Review

A Call for Women's Rights

A. As You Read

Directions: Answer the following questions as you read Section 3 in your textbook.

1. What rights did women lack in the mid-1800s?

   the right to vote, to own property, or to keep wages after marriage

2. Why was Sojourner Truth an effective leader in the fight for women's rights?

   She was a spellbinding speaker.

3. What was the purpose of the Seneca Falls Convention?

   to draw attention to the problems women faced; to demand equal rights for women

4. What educational opportunities did women have in the mid-1800s?

   Most poor women did not even learn to read. Middle-class girls learned only subjects such as dancing and singing.

   Some were able to attend the few colleges that accepted women.

B. Reviewing Key People

Directions: Briefly explain the contributions of each person to the campaign for women's rights.

5. the Grimké sisters campaigned for abolition and for women's rights

6. Sojourner Truth former slave who spoke out for women's rights all over the country

7. Lucretia Mott set up petition drives across the North for women's rights; helped organize the Seneca Falls Convention

8. Elizabeth Cady Stanton helped organize the Seneca Falls Convention

9. Susan B. Anthony traveled and spoke out for women's rights

10. Amelia Bloomer journalist who promoted comfortable, loose-fitting trousers ("bloomers") for women

11. Elizabeth Blackwell set an example for others by graduating from medical school and becoming a doctor

Name _____ Class _____ Date _____

Section 4 Guided Reading and Review
American Art and Literature

A. As You Read

Directions: As you read Section 4 in your textbook, complete the chart below by writing in the names of important American artists and writers in each category. Briefly identify each person. One example is given. *Possible answers below*

painting	1. Thomas Cole and Asher B. Durand, landscapes of Hudson River
	2. George Caleb Bingham, paintings of frontier life
	3. George Catlin and Alfred Jacob Miller, painters of American Indians in the West
poetry	4. Henry Wadsworth Longfellow, "Paul Revere's Ride" and "Hiawatha"
	5. John Greenleaf Whittier, poems on social issues
	6. Walt Whitman, *Leaves of Grass*
	7. Emily Dickinson, more than 1,700 poems, most of which were published after her death
novels and stories	8. Washington Irving, "Rip Van Winkle" and "The Legend of Sleepy Hollow"
	9. James Fenimore Cooper, historical novels about frontier life
	10. Herman Melville, *Moby-Dick*, a novel of whaling
	11. Nathaniel Hawthorne, *The Scarlet Letter*, historical novel of the Puritans in New England
	12. Edgar Allan Poe, many horror stories
	13. William Wells Brown, *Clotel*, a novel of slave life
	14. Catherine Sedgwick and Fanny Fern, best-selling novels about women
philosophy	15. Ralph Waldo Emerson, transcendentalist, essayist
	16. Henry David Thoreau, *Walden*, idea of civil disobedience

B. Reviewing Key Terms

Directions: Define the following terms.

17. transcendentalists _people who believed that the most important truths in life transcended, or went beyond, human reason_

18. civil disobedience _the idea that people have a right to disobey unjust laws if their consciences demand it_

Name _____ Class _____ Date _____

16 Section 1 Guided Reading and Review

Slavery in the Territories

A. As You Read

As you read Section 1 in your textbook, fill in the missing causes and effects.

Causes	Effects
Missouri applied for statehood as a slave state.	1. Congress agreed to admit Missouri as a slave state and Maine as a free state.
2. Congress passed the Missouri Compromise.	Slavery was legal in the Louisiana Purchase south of the Missouri border.
Many northerners opposed the spread of slavery into the West.	3. Congressman Wilmot called for a ban on slavery in territories won from Mexico.
4. The leaders of both political parties refused to take a firm stand on slavery.	People opposed to the spread of slavery founded the Free-Soil party.

B. Reviewing Key Terms

Explain the relevance of each term to the debate over slavery.

5. Missouri Compromise agreement that in the Louisiana Purchase, slavery would be legal in Missouri and south of the Missouri border and illegal north of it

_____

6. Wilmot Proviso proposal that slavery be banned in any territories ceded from Mexico; passed the House but not the Senate

_____

7. popular sovereignty rule of the people; the belief that citizens of new territories should decide for themselves whether to allow slavery

_____

8. Free-Soil party political party formed by those opposed to the spread of slavery into the West; formed because neither party took a firm stand on slavery

_____

Name _____ Class _____ Date _____

CHAPTER 16

Section 2 Guided Reading and Review
The Compromise of 1850

A. As You Read

As you read Section 2 in your textbook, answer the following questions: *Possible answers below*

1. Why were southerners against California's admission to the Union as a free state?

   California's admission would mean there were more free than slave states; southerners feared they would lose their power in Congress.

2. Why did congressmen believe that Henry Clay could resolve the debate? _____

   Clay had worked out the Missouri Compromise.

3. What was Calhoun's position on slavery in the West? *Calhoun favored slavery everywhere.*

   _____

4. Why was Daniel Webster willing to agree to a fugitive slave law? _____

   Webster believed that preserving the Union was the most important thing.

5. What were the five provisions of the Compromise of 1850? *California would be a free state;*

   New Mexico and Utah settlers would decide the slavery question for themselves; slave trade was abolished in

   Washington, D.C.; the fugitive slave act was passed; the border dispute between Texas and Mexico was resolved.

   _____

   _____

   _____

6. What was the northern reaction to the passage of the Fugitive Slave Act? _____

   Northerners were bitterly opposed to the act because most of them opposed slavery.

7. What effect did *Uncle Tom's Cabin* have on the nation? *It stirred up a passionate reaction against slavery in the North and resentment in the South because southerners believed that the book painted a false picture of slavery.*

B. Reviewing Key Terms

Briefly explain each person's contribution to the controversy over slavery.

8. Henry Clay *called for preservation of the Union; helped design the Compromise of 1850*

9. John C. Calhoun *spoke out in favor of slavery in the West; urged the South to leave the Union if compromise could not be reached*

10. Daniel Webster *called for preservation of the Union, even if this meant compromise over the slavery issue*

11. Stephen Douglas *took up Henry Clay's fight for the Compromise of 1850 when Clay became ill*

12. Harriet Beecher Stowe *wrote Uncle Tom's Cabin, international bestseller that drew people's attention to slavery and stirred up feeling against it*

Guided Reading and Review

Name _____ Class _____ Date _____

16 Section 3 Guided Reading and Review

The Crisis Deepens

A. As You Read

As you read Section 3 in your textbook, mark each statement true or false. Correct each false statement.

__False__ 1. Henry Clay suggested that the people of Kansas and Nebraska decide for themselves whether their territories would allow slavery.

    Replace Clay with Stephen Douglas.

__False__ 2. Southerners argued that the Kansas-Nebraska Act would overturn the Missouri Compromise.

    Replace southerners with northerners.

__True__ 3. Most people who moved to Kansas did so in search of cheap land.

__True__ 4. In 1855, Kansas ended up with two governments.

__False__ 5. A southern senator was severely beaten on the Senate floor for speaking out in favor of the Kansas legislature.

    Replace southern senator with northern senator.

__True__ 6. The Supreme Court ruled that the Missouri Compromise was unconstitutional.

B. Reviewing Key Terms

Write a sentence describing each person's role in the escalating battle over slavery.
Possible answers below

7. Stephen Douglas *Douglas sponsored the Kansas-Nebraska Act, which stated that popular sovereignty in each territory should decide the issue of slavery there.*

8. John Brown *Brown was an abolitionist who responded to a pro-slavery raid by massacring five pro-slavery settlers, arousing strong feelings on both sides of the slavery issue.*

9. Charles Sumner *Charles Sumner, a senator who spoke out bitterly against slavery, was severely beaten by a southern senator's nephew.*

10. Dred Scott *Dred Scott was a fugitive slave who sued for his freedom. The case went to the Supreme Court, which decided against him, thus rallying support for the abolitionist cause.*

11. Frederick Douglass *Douglass spoke out against the Dred Scott decision.*

CHAPTER

16 Section 4 Guided Reading and Review

The Republican Party Emerges

A. As You Read

As you read Section 4 in your textbook, complete each sentence. *Possible answers below*

1. The main goal of the new Republican party was to prevent slavery from spreading any farther.

2. The Republican candidate's popularity in the national election of 1856 made southerners afraid that their political power was declining.

3. The Senate campaign between Lincoln and Douglas received national attention because Douglas was expected to run for President in 1860.

4. Before running for the Senate, Lincoln grew up on the frontier, studied law, and served in the Illinois state legislature and in Congress.

5. At Harpers Ferry, John Brown raided a federal arsenal in an attempt to inspire a slave revolt; he was captured, tried, and executed.

B. Reviewing Key Terms

Match each person with his description.

___a___ 6. John C. Frémont

___b___ 7. James Buchanan

___d___ 8. Abraham Lincoln

___c___ 9. Stephen Douglas

___e___ 10. John Brown

a. first Republican candidate for President

b. Democrat who became President in 1856

c. Illinois senator who believed slavery question should be settled by popular sovereignty

d. Republican who ran for Illinois senate; gained national attention for his speeches against slavery

e. led what was planned to be a national slave uprising; tried for treason and executed

Name _____ Class _____ Date _____

16 Section 5 Guided Reading and Review
A Nation Divides

A. As You Read

As you read Section 5 in your textbook, list supporting ideas for each main idea below:
Possible answers below

> **Main Idea A:** The national election of 1860 reflected sectional divisions.
>
> 1. The Democratic party split into a northern and a southern party.
>
> 2. The Constitutional Union party received support in only a few southern states.
>
> 3. Abraham Lincoln, the Republican candidate for President, was not listed on the ballot in 10 southern states.
>
> **Main Idea B:** The South reacted strongly to the election results.
>
> 4. Southerners believed that Lincoln's victory meant that they would no longer have a voice in national government.
>
> 5. South Carolina's governor urged other southern states to secede from the Union.
>
> 6. In 1860 and 1861, several southern states seceded from the Union.
>
> 7. In April 1861, the Civil War began.

B. Reviewing Key Terms

Briefly identify the importance of each place to the 1860 elections and/or the start of the Civil War.

8. Chicago, Illinois site of the 1860 Republican national convention that nominated Lincoln for President

9. South Carolina the first state to suggest secession and the first state to secede

10. Fort Sumter site of the first shots of the Civil War

Name _____ Class _____ Date _____

CHAPTER

17 Section 1 Guided Reading and Review

The Conflict Takes Shape

A. As You Read

As you read Section 1 in your textbook, use the graphic organizer to compare and contrast the two sides fighting in the Civil War.

	United States of America	Confederate States of America
1. President	Abraham Lincoln	Jefferson Davis
2. Number of states	24	11
3. Reasons for fighting	to preserve the Union	to maintain slavery and southern way of life
4. Position on states' rights	believed in strong central government	believed in states' rights
5. Population	22 million	9 million; more than one third were slaves
6. Economy	industrial, able to manufacture supplies for war	agricultural, little industry, dependent on trade for arms, ammunition, and so on
7. Army	volunteer army raised from free citizens, unfamiliar with southern terrain	few free citizens to join army, good knowledge of terrain
8. Military leaders	Lincoln had trouble finding good generals	Robert E. Lee, West Point graduate

B. Reviewing Key Terms

Briefly define each term.

9. border state one of the four states—Kentucky, Missouri, Maryland, and Delaware—located along the border between the Union and the Confederate states

10. martial law rule by the army instead of the elected government

Guided Reading and Review

CHAPTER

17

Section 2 Guided Reading and Review

No Easy Victory

A. As You Read

As you read Section 2 in your textbook, answer the following questions. Possible answers below

1. What was the Union strategy for winning the war? The Union planned to use the navy to
blockade southern ports, capture the Confederate capital of Richmond, and take control of the Mississippi River.

2. Why did the Confederacy expect help from Europe? Southern cotton was important to
European textile mills; the South expected help from its trade partners.

3. Where and how did General Stonewall Jackson get his nickname? At the Battle of Bull
Run, someone observed that General Jackson had not retreated but was standing like a stone wall.

4. What did both sides learn from the Battle of Bull Run? that their soldiers were untrained
and that the war was likely to be long and violent

5. What kind of commander was General McClellan? well organized but hesitant to attack

6. What was the purpose of the Union blockade of southern ports? The Union did not want
supplies to get through to the South.

7. What was the United States Navy's contribution to the war? The navy blockaded southern
ports and took control of both ends of the Mississippi River.

B. Reviewing Key Terms

Briefly describe each battle, including the location and the winner.

8. Bull Run skirmish in Virginia in 1861; Stonewall Jackson's troops won the battle as Union soldiers ran away

9. Antietam two-day battle in Maryland between forces of Lee and McClellan; thousands died, and Confederates
retreated to Virginia; no clear winner

10. Fredericksburg victory in Virginia for Lee's troops; one of the Union's worst defeats

11. Chancellorsville victory for Lee's troops, but Stonewall Jackson died from Confederate fire

12. Shiloh battle won by Grant's Union troops in Tennessee

CHAPTER

17

Section 3 Guided Reading and Review

A Promise of Freedom

A. As You Read

As you read Section 3 in your textbook, complete the following sentences:

1. Lincoln approached the issue of emancipation cautiously because there were four slave
   states in the Union; not all citizens of the Union supported emancipation.

2. The Emancipation Proclamation stated that all slaves in the Confederacy would be freed as of
   January 1, 1863; this did not affect slaves in the United States.

3. European reaction to the Emancipation Proclamation was favorable; Europe would now be
   likely to support the Union in the Civil War.

4. African Americans fought in the Union army because the Union army supported abolition;
   they wanted to fight for slaves' right to freedom.

5. The 54th Massachusetts Regiment is famous because it showed great courage under fire,
   proving that African Americans were good soldiers.

6. Slaves in the Confederacy responded to the Emancipation Proclamation by _____
   slowing down or refusing to work, so as to weaken the Confederacy; hoping for a Union victory; escaping to the
   freedom the Union offered.

B. Reviewing Key Terms

Briefly explain the relevance of each term to the Civil War.

7. Emancipation Proclamation statement issued by President Lincoln that freed all slaves in
   the Confederacy

8. 54th Massachusetts Regiment all-black regiment that showed great courage under fire at Fort Wagner

9. Fort Wagner South Carolina fort; many members of 54th Massachusetts Regiment died attacking it

Name _____ Class _____ Date _____

Section 4 Guided Reading and Review

Hardships of War

A. As You Read

As you read Section 4 in your textbook, fill in supporting details for each main idea listed below: *Possible answers below*

Main Idea A: Army life was like a nightmare.

1. *Weapons were more deadly than ever before. Medical care was primitive at best, and conditions were unsanitary.*

2. *Soldiers had to sleep outdoors in all weather. Prisoners of war faced starvation and rampant disease.*

Main Idea B: Both sides faced difficulties on the home front.

3. *North: opposition to the military draft, rioting in cities, suspension of habeas corpus*
South: weak federal government, resentment over wealthy men's exemption from draft, not enough men
4. *to serve in army*

Main Idea C: The war affected the economy on both sides.

5. *North: established income tax to pay for war; inflation soared as more money was printed; farm production rose; many industries benefited from high demand*
6. *South: established taxes to pay for war; inflation soared as more money was printed; cotton trade collapsed; severe shortages of food, clothing, and supplies as a result of blockade*

Main Idea D: Women on both sides played an active role in the war.

7. *Women took over men's jobs; women's aid societies helped supply the troops; women held fundraising events.*

B. Reviewing Key Terms

Match each term with its definition.

___*b*___ 8. draft

___*a*___ 9. Copperhead

___*c*___ 10. inflation

___*d*___ 11. profiteer

a. northerner who opposed using force to keep the South in the Union

b. military service requirement

c. rise in prices and decrease in the value of money

d. manufacturer who charged excessive prices for goods that the government needed for war

CHAPTER

17

Section 5 Guided Reading and Review
The War Ends

A. As You Read

As you read Section 5 in your textbook, mark each statement true or false. Correct each false statement.

True 1. Lincoln appointed Grant commander of the army because Grant was efficient and an effective leader.

_____

False 2. A great victory at Vicksburg turned the tide of war <u>in the Confederacy's favor</u>.

in the Union's favor _____

True 3. Union control of the Mississippi cut the Confederacy in two.

_____

False 4. The Battle of Gettysburg was a decisive victory <u>for Robert E. Lee.</u>

for General Meade and the Union Army _____

False 5. The South would continue to fight <u>for a year</u> after the Battle of Gettysburg.

for two years _____

False 6. <u>Only five thousand men died</u> at the Battle of Gettysburg.

more than 50,000 died _____

True 7. Grant believed that total war against the southerners was the only way to win the war.

_____

False 8. Lee was forced to sign <u>harsh and inhuman terms of surrender</u> to the Union.

generous surrender terms _____

B. Reviewing Key Terms

Fill in each blank with the correct term.

9. Lincoln's brief speech in honor of the war dead is known as the ___*Gettysburg Address*___.

10. ___*Pickett's charge*___ was the last attack at Gettysburg, in which the Confederate soldiers were to cross open ground, climb a steep hill, and open fire on the enemy.

11. As part of the policy of ___*total war*___ against the South, railroads and crops were destroyed and cities were burned to the ground.

12. Lee surrendered to Grant at ___*Appomattox Court House*___.

Guided Reading and Review

CHAPTER

18 Section 1 Guided Reading and Review
Early Steps to Reunion

A. As You Read

As you read Section 1 in your textbook, answer the following questions: *Possible answers below*

1. Why was it harder for southerners than for northerners to adjust to peacetime?

   Fighting had devastated their cities and farmlands. Emancipation drastically changed their society. Their economy was in ruins. The North was largely untouched by the fighting, its social institutions were not affected, and its economy recovered quickly.

2. What were Lincoln's intentions toward the South after the war ended? *He devised a Ten Percent Plan in which a southern state could form a new government if ten percent of its citizens took a loyalty oath to the United States. He offered pardons to all Confederates who swore this oath.*

3. (a) What was the main goal of the Freedmen's Bureau? (b) What services did it provide?

   (a) to help former slaves (b) It provided food and clothing, helped freedmen find jobs, and set up schools for them. It also provided medical care for both freedmen and poor whites.

4. What effect did Lincoln's assassination have on the United States?

   The country was plunged into grief.

5. What did Andrew Johnson do when he became President? *He approved new southern state governments after required loyalty oaths were sworn and the states ratified the Thirteenth Amendment, which abolished slavery.*

B. Reviewing Key Terms

Match each description at the left with a term or name at the right.

_b_ 6. rebuilding of the South after the Civil War

_e_ 7. required majority of white men in former Confederate states to swear loyalty to the Union

_c_ 8. agency that aided former slaves

_a_ 9. actor who shot President Lincoln and died soon after while hiding from police

_d_ 10. abolished slavery throughout the United States

a. John Wilkes Booth

b. Reconstruction

c. Freedmen's Bureau

d. Thirteenth Amendment

e. Wade-Davis Bill

CHAPTER

18 Section 2 Guided Reading and Review
Radical Reconstruction

A. As You Read

As you read Section 2 in your textbook, complete each sentence. *Possible answers below*

1. Southern legislatures' response to the Thirteenth Amendment was to pass "black codes" that denied African Americans many of their rights as citizens.

2. Republicans were outraged at the black codes and President Johnson because they believed that Johnson was allowing the South to bring back many of the worst characteristics of slavery.

3. Radical Republicans' two chief goals were to break the power of wealthy southern planters and to ensure that freedmen could exercise their right to vote.

4. The Fourteenth Amendment stated that all persons born in the United States were citizens and that no state could deprive a person of life, liberty, or property without due process of law.

5. The 1866 elections resulted in Republican majorities in both houses of Congress.

6. The Reconstruction Act required that former Confederate states ratify the Fourteenth Amendment, write new constitutions, and allow African Americans to vote; it also established martial law in the South.

7. President Johnson was impeached because he tried to limit the effect of the Radical Reconstruction program.

8. Republicans supported the Fifteenth Amendment because they honored African American rights, they thought that northern African Americans should be treated equally with those in the South, and they knew that African Americans would vote Republican.

B. Reviewing Key Terms

Briefly identify the following terms.

9. Radical Reconstruction restructuring of southern society by the 1867 Congress

10. black codes laws that severely limited rights of freedmen in the South

CHAPTER

18 Section 3 Guided Reading and Review

The South Under Reconstruction

A. As You Read

As you read Section 3 in your textbook, fill in the missing causes and effects.

Causes	Effects
1. Northerners wanted to help the freedmen, to profit from the rebuilding of the South, and to settle in a pleasant place.	Many northerners came South after the war.
African Americans in the South went to the polls in large numbers.	2. Numerous African Americans were elected to public office, including some to Congress.
3. White southern Democrats resisted Reconstruction and change.	Some southerners formed a terrorist group called the Ku Klux Klan.
Reconstruction governments spent a lot of money on railroads, school systems, and telegraph lines.	4. Southern governments raised income taxes to pay for improvements.
5. Freedmen had few opportunities.	Most freedmen worked the land and remained poor.

B. Reviewing Key Terms

Match each term with its definition.

___b___ 6. scalawag

___c___ 7. carpetbagger

___a___ 8. sharecropper

a. farmer who rented land and was given seeds, fertilizer, and tools in return for a share of the crop at harvest time

b. southern Democrat's derogatory nickname for southern Republican

c. northerner who went to the South after the war

Name _____ Class _____ Date _____

CHAPTER

18 Section 4 Guided Reading and Review

The End of Reconstruction

A. As You Read

As you read Section 4 in your textbook, fill in supporting details for each of the main ideas listed below. *Possible answers below*

Main Idea A: Reconstruction came to an end in the 1870s.

1. Corruption in Washington made the Republican party unpopular.

2. The Amnesty Act restored the right to vote to white southerners.

3. President Hayes removed federal troops from the South.

Main Idea B: After Reconstruction ended, African Americans in the South began losing their rights.

4. Southern states passed legislation requiring literacy tests and payment of a fee for each vote; most African Americans could not pass the tests or pay the fees.

5. Segregation became legal throughout the South after 1877.

Main Idea C: Industries flourished in the New South.

6. The South began building textile mills and tobacco refineries.

7. The South tapped into its mineral resources.

B. Reviewing Key Terms

Briefly explain the relevance of each of the following terms to the end of the Reconstruction era.

8. poll tax tax required for all voters; established to prevent poor freedmen from voting

9. literacy test test to prove ability to read; designed to ban illiterate freedmen from voting

10. grandfather clause clause stating that all those whose fathers or grandfathers had voted before 1867 did not have to take the literacy test; designed to make more whites eligible to vote

11. segregation separation by race; designed to ban freedmen from equal access to public and private facilities

12. *Plessy* v. *Ferguson* Supreme Court decision that segregation was legal if separate facilities were equal; permitted segregation to continue

Guided Reading and Review

CHAPTER

19

Section 1 Guided Reading and Review

Indian Peoples of the Great Plains

A. As You Read

As you read Section 1 in your textbook, complete the graphic organizer by filling in supporting details for each main idea. *Possible answers below*

Main Idea A: Horses and buffalo played a central role in the culture of the Plains Indians.

1. After the Pueblos drove out the Spaniards in 1680, they were left with thousands of Spanish horses.

2. Plains Indians traded for these horses.

3. Plains Indians used horses for hunting, moving their villages, and going on raids.

4. Buffalo was the main source of food for Plains Indians.

5. Buffalo hides provided Plains Indians with shelter and clothing.

Main Idea B: Men's and women's activities and duties differed.

6. Women occasionally took part in hunting and governing.

7. Women gathered food and took care of children.

8. Women made tepees, clothing, baskets, and blankets.

9. Men hunted buffalo and taught boys to hunt.

10. Men led religious ceremonies.

11. Men provided military leadership.

B. Reviewing Key Places

Match each term with its definition.

__d__ 12. tepee   a. sled pulled by a dog or horse

__a__ 13. travois   b. dried buffalo meat

__c__ 14. corral   c. enclosure for livestock

__b__ 15. jerky   d. tent made by stretching buffalo skins on tall poles

CHAPTER

19 Section 2 Guided Reading and Review

Mining and Railroading

A. As You Read

As you read Section 2 in your textbook, list one cause and one effect of each of the following events: *Possible answers below*

1. Miners began to leave boomtowns.

Cause: They had stripped the local mines of all the gold and silver.

Effect: The boomtown became a ghost town.

2. Few miners ever got rich.

Cause: Much of the gold and silver was deep underground and could be reached only with costly machinery.

Effect: Most mining was taken over by large companies that could afford the equipment.

3. Lawlessness and disorder often were characteristics of boomtowns.

Cause: Towns grew rapidly and without organized government.

Effect: Vigilante groups were formed to enforce laws.

4. Construction of a transcontinental railroad was completed in 1869.

Cause: Now that the entire continent was settled by European Americans, they wanted an efficient way to travel and transport goods.

Effect: Travel became much faster and more common; population boomed in the western territories, which quickly became states.

B. Reviewing Key Terms

Briefly define each term.

5. lode rich vein of gold or silver

6. vigilante self-appointed law enforcer

7. transcontinental railroad a railroad that stretches across a continent from coast to coast

8. subsidy financial aid or a land grant from the government

Name _____ Class _____ Date _____

Section 3 Guided Reading and Review
The Cattle Kingdom

A. As You Read

As you read Section 3 in your textbook, describe each of the following in two or three sentences: *Possible answers below*

1. cowhand A cowhand worked with cattle, driving them along trails like the Chisholm Trail from the southwest to the midwestern railroads on which they would be shipped east and slaughtered. Cowhands worked in groups, riding with the herds and keeping them together. Cowhands worked in all kinds of weather, often for 18 hours at a stretch, and earned very little money.

2. cattle drive A cattle drive was the long journey from the southwest to the railroads. Cowhands herded cattle along the way. The dangers on a cattle drive included stampedes, thunderstorms, rattlesnakes, and prairie dog holes, which could break an animal's leg.

3. cow town A cow town was a community that sprang up along the trail of the cattle drive. In a cow town, cattle were penned up in enclosures until they could be shipped east. The cowhands could rest and refresh themselves in dance halls, saloons, and restaurants. Cow towns also included ordinary settlers, such as barbers, doctors, bankers, and merchants.

B. Reviewing Key Terms

Fill in the blanks with the correct terms.

4. A _____cattle drive_____ was a long journey of cattle from the Southwest to railroad lines in Kansas and Missouri.

5. A _____vaquero_____ was a skilled Mexican rider who herded cattle on Southwestern ranches.

6. A _____lariat_____ is used to lasso cattle.

7. _____Chaps_____ protected a rider's legs from thorny plants.

8. A gunshot or clap of thunder could start a _____stampede_____, in which cattle set off at a run.

9. A _____cow town_____ was a town in which cattle were held until they could be shipped east.

CHAPTER

19

Section 4 Guided Reading and Review

Indian Peoples in Retreat

A. As You Read

As you read Section 4 in your textbook, answer the following questions: Possible answers below

1. What were the terms of the Fort Laramie Treaty? Native American nations agreed to keep to a limited area of land in return for money, domestic animals, agricultural tools and goods, and a permanent right to that land.

2. What happened at the Chivington Massacre? Colonel John Chivington and a band of settlers slaughtered more than 200 Cheyenne.

3. What happened to the buffalo of the Great Plains? Disease, drought, habitat destruction, and sport hunting killed most of them off.

4. What was the cause of the Sioux War of 1876? Gold was found in the Black Hills; miners invaded Native American lands to get the gold.

5. What happened at the Battle of Little Bighorn? The Lakota and Cheyenne Indians killed Colonel Custer and all his troops.

6. What effect did the Ghost Dance have on non-Native Americans? It scared them because they thought that it meant that the Native Americans were preparing to go to war.

7. What happened at Wounded Knee Creek? The American army killed nearly 300 Lakota who were trying to surrender.

8. What was the intention of the Dawes Act? to encourage Native Americans to become farmers

B. Reviewing Key Terms

Briefly identify each person listed below.

9. Sitting Bull   Lakota chief and holy man who led his people in the Sioux War and was shot during an attempted arrest

10. John Chivington   army colonel who ordered the massacre of Cheyenne at a fort to which they had come for help

11. George Armstrong Custer   army colonel who was killed at Little Bighorn

12. Chief Joseph   Nez Percé chief who led his people on a long retreat to Canada; surrendered short of the border because his people were dying

13. Geronimo   Apache leader who became a fierce warrior against the settlers who tried to steal Apache lands

14. Susette La Flesche   Omaha chief's daughter who wrote and lectured about the destruction of the Native American way of life

15. Helen Hunt Jackson   author of A Century of Dishonor, early history of the treatment of Native American tribes by the United States

Name _____ Class _____ Date _____

19 Section 5 Guided Reading and Review
Farming

A. As You Read

As you read Section 5 in your textbook, complete the following sentences:

1. To encourage people to settle the West, the government passed the
   <u>Homestead Act of 1862</u> .

2. African American homesteaders called themselves the ____<u>Exodusters</u>____ after
   a book of the Bible that described the Jewish flight from slavery in Egypt.

3. The first farmers to settle Oklahoma were called _____<u>Sooners</u>_____ because
   they grabbed their land before the official date.

4. Dangers caused by the dry climate of the Plains included <u>crop failure, swarms of grass-</u>
   <u>hoppers, and grass fires.</u>

5. Women's duties on the Plains farms included <u>cooking, doctoring, teaching, raising children,</u>
   <u>cleaning, making soap, making candles, sewing clothing and bedding.</u>

6. Farmers formed the National Grange and the Farmer's Alliance because _____
   <u>they wanted to raise their profits and reduce shipping costs.</u>

7. The Populist party supported these ideas: <u>governmental help for falling prices, regulation of</u>
   <u>railroad rates, income tax, an eight-hour workday, limits on immigration.</u>

B. Reviewing Key Terms

Briefly explain the relevance of each term to the settlement of the West.

8. sod house <u>Because there were few trees on the Great Plains, settlers made their houses of soil held together</u>
   <u>by grass roots.</u>

9. sodbuster <u>The soil of the Great Plains was so hard that it took a steel sodbusting plow to farm it. Plains</u>
   <u>farmers thus became known as sodbusters.</u>

10. cooperative <u>In 1867, the National Grange set up the first cooperatives, in which farmers pooled their money</u>
    <u>to buy tools and seeds more economically.</u>

11. wholesale <u>Wholesale is buying or selling large quantities of goods at lower prices.</u>

CHAPTER

20

Section 1 Guided Reading and Review

Railroads Spur Industry

A. As You Read

As you read Section 1 in your textbook, explain the importance of each of the following developments in the national railroad on American society and on the economy.

Possible answers below

1. In 1886, Southern railroads adopted the Northern gauge. _All trains in the United States now could run on all tracks._

2. George Westinghouse invented the air brake. _The air brake allowed an engineer to stop all the cars at once, so trains became longer and faster, and travel was much safer._

3. Companies began buying up small rail lines. _Railroad owners made vast fortunes, and more and more miles of track were controlled by fewer and fewer people._

4. Many industries boomed because of the railroad. _Steel workers supplied iron for railroad tracks. Loggers cut down trees and made the wood rail ties. Miners dug coal that fueled train engines. The railroad itself became a major industry._

B. Reviewing Key Terms

Use each term correctly in an accurate statement about the growth of the railroad.

Possible answers below

5. gauge _Only when all tracks were made to the same gauge, or width, could all trains run on all tracks in the United States._

6. network _The network of connected rail lines became possible when all tracks were laid to a uniform gauge._

7. consolidate _Many companies began to consolidate, or combine, their rail lines to make the system more efficient._

8. rebate _Often railroads granted rebates, or discounts, on shipping rates to their biggest customers._

9. pool _To raise prices, railroads created a pool in which they shared the business within a given area._

CHAPTER

20

Section 2 Guided Reading and Review

The Rise of Big Business

A. As You Read

As you read Section 2 in your textbook, fill in the missing causes and effects.

Causes	Effects
The Bessemer process allowed stronger steel to be produced more cheaply.	1. Railroads began making steel rails; architects began building skyscrapers.
2. Carnegie gained control over all aspects of steel production.	Carnegie had a great advantage over other steel producers.
J. P. Morgan invested in troubled corporations.	3. As a major shareholder, Morgan could influence company policy in his own interest.
Rockefeller knew that oil was not profitable until it was refined.	4. Rockefeller built an oil refinery.
5. Congress passed the Sherman Antitrust Act, which banned trusts and monopolies.	Corporations usually found ways to avoid regulations.

B. Reviewing Key Terms

Match each person with his description.

__a__ 6. Henry Bessemer

__b__ 7. Andrew Carnegie

__d__ 8. J. P. Morgan

__c__ 9. John D. Rockefeller

a. discovered a new way to convert iron into steel

b. Scottish immigrant to the United States who made a fortune in steel mills

c. built up his oil refineries into the Standard Oil Company of Ohio

d. banker who eventually gained control of U.S. Steel

CHAPTER
20
Section 3 Guided Reading and Review
Inventions Change the Nation

A. As You Read

As you read Section 3 in your textbook, correct each of the following false statements:

Possible answers below

1. The telephone was an instant success. At first, people thought of the telephone as a toy; eventually its inventor made a fortune.

2. Movies became possible with the invention of the light bulb. Movies were made possible when projectors were invented.

3. Assembly lines made it possible for people to eat fresh meat. Refrigeration made it possible to ship perishable goods long distances so that people could have fresh meat year-round.

4. Henry Ford charged less for his cars because he didn't care about making a profit. Ford's cars were cheaper because the assembly line process made them cheaper to produce.

5. The first airplane could fly 40 miles per hour and was used for wartime reconnaissance. The first airplane flew 120 feet in 12 seconds.

B. Reviewing Key Terms

Identify the invention or inventions for which each of the following people is known.

6. Elisha Otis passenger elevator brake

7. Thomas Edison light bulb, phonograph, movie projector

8. Alexander Graham Bell telephone

9. Lewis E. Waterman fountain pen

10. King C. Gillette safety razor with disposable blades

11. George Pullman railroad sleeping car

CHAPTER

20  Section 4 Guided Reading and Review

The Rise of Organized Labor

A. As You Read

As you read Section 4 in your textbook, answer the following questions: *Possible answers below*

1. How did the relationship between worker and boss change after the Civil War?

   The relationship became less personal as factories grew larger and machines did much of the skilled work.

2. What were the results of the 1885 strike at the Missouri Pacific Railroad?

   The railroad canceled a cut in wages; the strike was seen as a victory for the Knights of Labor, whose

   membership soared.

3. What happened in Haymarket Square when workers clashed with strikebreakers?

   Police killed four workers. During a protest the following day, a bomb went off and seven police officers were killed.

   Anarchists were tried and convicted of the crime.

4. What were the goals of the American Federation of Labor?

   to obtain higher wages, shorter hours, and better working conditions for its members and to obtain the right to

   negotiate on behalf of workers

5. What is Mother Jones best known for?

   Mary Harris Jones spoke publicly about child labor, helping to achieve reforms.

6. Why is the Triangle Shirtwaist Company fire significant in the labor movement?

   The Triangle fire gained enough publicity and shocked enough people that it inspired many states to pass safety

   laws for factories.

7. Why were unions not popular in the United States in the late 1800s?

   Frequent strikes for wages disrupted services, and many people believed that unions were run by

   foreign-born radicals.

B. Reviewing Key Terms

Complete each sentence below by writing the correct term in the blank.

8. A _____ sweatshop _____ is a workplace in which people labor long hours in poor conditions for low pay.

9. A _____ strikebreaker _____ replaces a worker who has gone on strike.

10. _____ Collective bargaining _____ is the right of unions to negotiate with management on behalf of a group of workers.

11. The initials _____ ILGWU _____ stand for the famous union of garment workers that was founded in 1900.

Name _____ Class _____ Date _____

 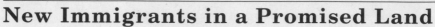

Section 1 Guided Reading and Review

New Immigrants in a Promised Land

A. As You Read

As you read Section 1 in your textbook, fill in the following chart with details about immigration in the late 1800s. *Possible answers below*

	Immigration
1. place of origin	Europe, Russia, Mexico, Asia, Greece, Ottoman Empire
2. reasons for resettling	religious persecution, political unrest, poverty at home, promise of industrial jobs, promise of religious and political freedom
3. journey to the United States	From Europe or Asia, people traveled in steerage below the decks of large ships crossing the ocean. Disease spread rapidly, and many died on the voyage.
4. life in the United States	Most immigrants settled in cities because of the factory jobs available there. Groups of immigrants from the same country tended to form neighborhoods in cities, thus maintaining their language and culture. Children quickly learned English in school.
5. American response	Many Americans objected to the influx of foreign cultures and the immigrants' willingness to work for low wages. The Chinese Exclusion Act barred Chinese from entering the United States; a later bill banned all who could not read their own language.

B. Reviewing Key Terms

Briefly identify each of the following terms.

6. pogrom organized attacks on Jewish villages in Russia

7. steerage airless area below the deck of a large ship

8. Statue of Liberty symbol of hope and freedom for immigrants sailing into New York Harbor

9. acculturation the process of holding on to older traditions while adapting to a new culture

10. nativist one who wants to limit immigration and preserve the United States for American-born white Protestants

Guided Reading and Review

CHAPTER

21

Section 2 Guided Reading and Review
An Age of Cities

A. As You Read

As you read Section 2 in your textbook, mark each statement true or false. Correct each false statement.

False 1. By 1890, the majority of Americans lived in cities.

One in three lived in cities.

True 2. Many African Americans migrated to northern cities to escape prejudice and find work.

_____

True 3. Many slum apartments had no windows, heating, or indoor bathrooms.

_____

False 4. The rich, the middle classes, and the urban poor all lived in the same neighborhoods.

Each social class lived in distinct neighborhoods.

True 5. Unpleasant aspects of city life included garbage, pollution, and pickpockets.

_____

False 6. Religious organizations founded settlement houses to help the poor.

Settlement houses were secular; religious organizations did other work to help the poor.

False 7. Jane Addams is best known for helping to establish professional police and fire departments in Chicago.

She is best known for founding Hull House, Chicago's famous settlement house.

B. Reviewing Key Terms

Complete each sentence.

8. _____Urbanization_____ meant that cities were becoming more and more crowded.

9. Only the poorest people in a city would live in a _____tenement_____, with its lack of air, heat, and sanitation.

10. By the 1880s, _____building codes_____ set standards for construction and safety of city housing.

11. The _____Salvation Army_____ spread the teachings of Christianity but also offered food and shelter to the poor.

12. The _____Young Men's Hebrew Association (YMHA)_____ helped preserve Jewish culture and provided community services.

CHAPTER 21

Section 3 Guided Reading and Review

Life in the Changing Cities

A. As You Read

As you read Section 3 in your textbook, complete the graphic organizer by filling in supporting details for each main idea. *Possible answers below*

Main Idea A: A building boom made remarkable changes to city life.

1. Architects began building skyscrapers with elevators to carry passengers to the upper floors.

2. Electric streetcars and subways eased street traffic.

3. Public parks preserved open green space for city dwellers to enjoy.

Main Idea B: New diversions in cities made life there much more entertaining and fun.

4. Department stores offered all kinds of goods under one roof.

5. Organized sports, like baseball, drew many fans to watch the games.

6. Professional theater and concerts entertained people everywhere.

B. Reviewing Key Terms

Briefly define each term.

7. skyscraper   a tall building with many floors supported by a steel frame

8. suburb   a residential area on or near the outskirts of a city

9. department store   a store selling all kinds of goods in different sections or departments

10. vaudeville   a variety show that included comedians, song-and-dance performers, and acrobats

11. ragtime   music with a lively, rhythmic sound

Name _____ Class _____ Date _____

Section 4 Guided Reading and Review
Public Education and American Culture

A. As You Read

As you read Section 4 in your textbook, fill in the missing causes and effects.

Causes	Effects
An industrial society needed educated workers.	1. Many states passed compulsory education laws.
2. As education spread, people spent more time reading.	The number of newspapers grew dramatically.
Girls as well as boys were sent to school and taught to read.	3. Magazines and newspapers competed for female readers.
4. Many new novels were written by realists.	Realists wanted to show the costs of urbanization and industrial growth.
5. Mark Twain's stories and novels poked fun at serious issues.	Mark Twain's stories and novels were widely popular.

B. Reviewing Key Terms

Match each person with his or her description.

___e___ 6. Joseph Pulitzer

___g___ 7. William Randolph Hearst

___a___ 8. Horatio Alger

___i___ 9. Stephen Crane

___f___ 10. Kate Chopin

___c___ 11. Mark Twain

___h___ 12. Winslow Homer

___d___ 13. Thomas Eakins

___b___ 14. Mary Cassatt

a. author of more than 100 rags-to-riches stories for children

b. moved to France and painted everyday scenes of mothers and children

c. writer of satirical stories and novels about serious issues

d. painter of medical and sporting scenes

e. publisher of the New York *World*

f. writer of stories about life in New Orleans

g. publisher of the New York *Journal*

h. painter of realistic scenes of New England coast

i. realist writer of *The Red Badge of Courage*

CHAPTER

22 Section 1 Guided Reading and Review

Reform in the Gilded Age

A. As You Read

Directions: As you read Section 1 in your textbook, answer the following questions:

Possible answers below

1. What two concerns shaped politics in the Gilded Age? *One was the power the wealthy class had acquired. The other was bribery, corruption, and voter fraud.*

2. What did President Hayes do about corruption at the New York customhouse?

   He ordered an investigation and fired two officials.

3. What did the Pendleton Act create? *the Civil Service Commission, which established exams for all those applying for federal jobs*

4. What did the Interstate Commerce Act of 1887 do? *It banned pools and rebates and set up a commission to oversee the railroads.*

5. What were the results of the passage of the Sherman Antitrust Act? *At first, judges ruled in favor of trusts and against labor unions. Later, they began to use the act to rule against monopolies.*

B. Reviewing Key Terms

Directions: Explain the relevance of each term to reform in the Gilded Age. *Possible answers below*

6. patronage *Patronage, the gift of jobs to political supporters, was common under the spoils system.*

7. merit *Spoils system reforms included putting programs in place to ensure the awarding of government jobs based on merit.*

8. civil service *The civil service is made up of all government workers except elected officials and the military. Creating the Civil Service Commission ensured that civil servants would be chosen on the basis of merit.*

9. interstate commerce *Interstate commerce, or trade between states, was first regulated by the Interstate Commerce Commission during the Gilded Age.*

CHAPTER

22

Section 2 Guided Reading and Review
The Progressives

A. As You Read
Directions: As you read Section 2 in your textbook, correct each false statement.

1. Political bosses fought corruption at all levels of government. _Political bosses controlled_ _voters' loyalty and thus "bought" politicians and created corruption._

2. Muckraking journalists ignored the need for reform. _Muckraking journalists pushed for reform_ _by exposing the evils of politics and big business._

3. The Progressives were a unified political party. _The Progressives included many groups and_ _individuals who were united only by their belief that the government should act for the public good._

4. Robert La Follette's actions helped increase railroad rates. _Robert La Follette lowered_ _railroad rates, thereby increasing rail traffic and helping both owners and passengers._

5. The Supreme Court decreed that after 1912, senators would be elected by the people instead of by legislatures. _Congress passed the Seventeenth Amendment in 1912, stating that senators_ _would be elected by the people instead of by legislatures._

B. Reviewing Key Terms
Directions: Match each person with his or her description.

Column I

___f___ 6. Thomas Nast

___d___ 7. William Tweed

___a___ 8. Jacob Riis

___e___ 9. Ida Tarbell

___b___ 10. Upton Sinclair

___g___ 11. John Dewey

___c___ 12. Robert La Follette

Column II

a. journalist and photographer who exposed slum conditions in New York

b. author of *The Jungle,* which exposed the meatpacking industry

c. Wisconsin governor who introduced reforms

d. corrupt political boss of New York City

e. journalist who exposed the Standard Oil Company

f. newspaper cartoonist who satirized corrupt politicians

g. Progressive educator

CHAPTER

22 Section 3 Guided Reading and Review

Progressives in the White House

A. As You Read

Directions: As you read Section 3 in your textbook, compare and contrast the three Progressive Presidents by filling in details about each. *Possible answers below*

1. Theodore Roosevelt	fought successfully to break up bad trusts, sided with labor against management, reformed railroads and meatpacking industry, protected wilderness
2. William Howard Taft	broke up trusts, approved safety rules for mines, established the eight-hour day for workers, raised tariffs
3. Woodrow Wilson	lowered tariffs, fought trusts, persuaded Congress to create the FTC, signed Clayton Antitrust Act

B. Reviewing Key Terms

Directions: Briefly identify each reform, specifying which President established each. Mark an R for Roosevelt, a T for Taft, or a W for Wilson.

__R__ 4. Square Deal social system that gave everyone an equal chance to succeed

__R__ 5. Pure Food and Drug Act required food and drug producers to list ingredients on packages

__W__ 6. New Freedom program that supported free enterprise system

__W__ 7. Federal Reserve Act set up a system of federal banks and gave government control of money supply

__W__ 8. Federal Trade Commission had the power to investigate companies and stop them from using unfair practices against competitors

CHAPTER

22 Section 4 Guided Reading and Review
Women Win Reforms

A. As You Read
Directions: As you read Section 4 in your textbook, complete each sentence.

1. The Seneca Falls Convention was the beginning of the organized women's rights movement.
_____

2. Western states granted women the right to vote because these states recognized the
contributions of pioneer women.

3. Carrie Chapman Catt helped the cause of suffrage by creating a plan to fight for suffrage
state by state.

4. While picketing outside the White House, Alice Paul, Rose Winslow, and others
were arrested and jailed, drawing public support for their cause.
_____

5. Women's clubs contributed to the fight for rights by providing women with opportunities to
gather, talk, discuss issues, and plan reforms.

6. Women supported the temperance drive because drinking threatened the family's safety and
economic stability.

B. Reviewing Key Terms
Directions: Match each term or person with the correct description.

Column I

_f_	7.	Carrie Chapman Catt
_c_	8.	suffragist
_e_	9.	Alice Paul
_b_	10.	Nineteenth Amendment
_d_	11.	Carrie Nation
_a_	12.	Eighteenth Amendment

Column II

a. banned the sale of alcoholic drinks

b. gave women the right to vote

c. one who fought for women's right to vote

d. radical temperance advocate

e. often arrested for her marches and protests in favor of suffrage for women

f. organized a plan to fight for women's suffrage one state at a time

CHAPTER

22

Section 5 Guided Reading and Review

Other Americans Seek Justice

A. As You Read

Directions: As you read Section 5 in your textbook, fill in the outline with details describing the experience of each ethnic group during the Progressive era.
Possible answers below

Main Idea A: African Americans

1. lost many rights because of segregation and Jim Crow laws
2. faced lynchings
3. set up trade schools for African Americans and created the NAACP

Main Idea B: Mexican Americans

4. manual laborers
5. preserved language and culture
6. formed mutual aid groups

Main Idea C: Asian Americans

7. hard-working farmers
8. faced segregation in some areas

Main Idea D: Native Americans

9. forced onto mainly barren reservations
10. set up Society of American Indians to fight for Indian rights

B. Reviewing Key Terms

Directions: Briefly define or identify each term.

11. lynch murder by a mob

12. NAACP National Association for the Advancement of Colored People; group that fought for rights of African Americans

13. barrio Mexican neighborhood

14. Gentleman's Agreement informal agreement that the United States would allow Japanese women to join their husbands in the United States if Japan sent no further workers to the United States

Name _____ Class _____ Date _____

Section 1 Guided Reading and Review

A Pacific Empire

A. As You Read

Directions: As you read Section 1 in your textbook, use the chart to compare and contrast the relationships between the United States and the nations listed.
Possible answers below

1. Japan	An expedition led by Matthew Perry persuaded Japan to begin trade with the United States in 1854.
2. Russia	The United States purchased the vast territory of Alaska from Russia in 1867.
3. Samoa	The United States, Germany, and Britain all wanted Samoa because of its harbor. The United States eventually gained part of Samoa in a treaty.
4. Hawaii	American missionaries sailed to Hawaii in 1820. Later American travelers established a sugar industry there. In 1893, the United States forced the monarch to give up her throne. The United States annexed Hawaii in 1898.
5. China	The United States persuaded other nations to let trade with China be open to all. American soldiers helped end the Boxer Rebellion of 1900.

B. Reviewing Key Terms

Directions: Use each term correctly in an accurate statement about the policy and actions of the United States in the Pacific. Possible answers below

6. isolationism George Washington had encouraged a policy of isolationism, which kept the United States free from involvement in foreign affairs.

7. expansionism The United States had always pursued a policy of westward expansionism, adding new states and extending its boundaries.

8. annex Monarchists probably protested the successful American attempt to annex the kingdom of Hawaii.

9. imperialism During the Age of Imperialism, powerful countries took control of weaker ones, creating vast empires.

10. sphere of influence Britain was one of several countries that maintained a sphere of influence in China, enjoying its special trade privileges.

CHAPTER

23 Section 2 Guided Reading and Review
War With Spain

A. As You Read

Directions: As you read Section 2 in your textbook, answer the following questions:
Possible answers below

1. Why did President McKinley declare war on Spain? McKinley gave in to a combination of public pressure to support the rebels and the desire to protect American trade in the Caribbean.

2. What was the cause of the Cuban rebellion of 1895? Cubans wanted control over their own land and government.

3. What was the reaction of the United States to the rebellion in Cuba? Most Americans supported the rebels because they too had fought for independence.

4. How did the newspapers of the day affect the situation? The papers printed exaggerated stories and outright lies to whip up popular support for American intervention in the rebellion.

5. Why did the Americans fight in the Philippines? The Philippines were home to Spain's Pacific naval base.

6. What was the outcome of the Spanish-American War? Cuba became independent. The United States acquired Puerto Rico and Guam. The United States purchased the Philippines from Spain for $20 million.

B. Reviewing Key Terms

Directions: Identify each person's role in the Spanish-American War.

7. William McKinley   American President; reluctantly declared war on Spain

8. José Martí   Cuban who spoke publicly for independence; was killed early in the fighting

9. Joseph Pulitzer   owner/publisher of New York World; published exaggerated stories of Spanish atrocities in Cuba to whip up public support for war

10. William Randolph Hearst   owner/publisher of New York Journal; published exaggerated stories of Spanish atrocities in Cuba to whip up public support for war

11. Theodore Roosevelt   Assistant Secretary of the Navy; made decision to attack Philippines; fought with "Rough Riders" cavalry regiment in Cuba

12. George Dewey   commander of Pacific fleet; destroyed Spanish fleet in Philippines

13. John J. Pershing   commander of 10th Cavalry, African American regiment that took San Juan Hill in Cuba

Name _____ Class _____ Date _____

Section 3 Guided Reading and Review
The United States in Latin America

A. As You Read

Directions: As you read Section 3 in your textbook, complete the following sentences:
Possible answers below

1. President Roosevelt wanted to build a canal across Panama because it would benefit

   American commerce and military capability by providing a shortcut from the Atlantic to the Pacific.

2. The greatest obstacle to the workers digging the canal was disease carried by mosquitoes.

   _____

3. Merchants and manufacturers benefited from the building of the Panama Canal because

   it allowed them to ship goods cheaply to Asia and South America.

   _____

4. Roosevelt extended the Monroe Doctrine to state that the United States had a right to

   intervene in Latin America to preserve law and order.

5. The United States wanted to keep Europe out of Latin America because it did not

   want European countries meddling in Latin American affairs.

6. The United States invested in Latin America because it wanted to build strong economic

   ties and increase trade.

7. Relations between the United States and Mexico grew strained because the United

   States intervened in the Mexican civil war.

B. Reviewing Key Terms

Directions: Match each term with its definition.

Column I	Column II
__c__ 8. isthmus	a. policy of building strong economic ties between nations
__b__ 9. corollary	b. addition
__a__ 10. dollar diplomacy	c. strip of land connecting two larger bodies of land

CHAPTER 24 ★ Section 1 Guided Reading and Review
War in Europe

A. As You Read

Directions: As you read Section 1 in your textbook, list one cause and one effect of each of the following events: *Possible answers below*

1. European nationalists demanded freedom and self-government.

   Cause: They believed that oppressed people should overthrow foreign rulers and rule themselves.

   Effect: creation of mistrust and rivalry between nations

2. The Archduke of Austria-Hungary and his wife were assassinated in Sarajevo in 1914.

   Cause: A Serbian terrorist group wanted Austria to grant Bosnia its independence.

   Effect: Austria-Hungary declared war on Serbia.

3. Germany declared war on Russia and France.

   Cause: Germany and Austria-Hungary were allies; Russia had ordered its army to prepare for war.

   Effect: The Germans marched through Belgium, and Britain, Belgium's ally, declared war on Germany.

4. Neither side gained much territory during four years of trench warfare.

   Cause: In trench warfare, troops dig themselves in, and it is difficult to dislodge them.

   Effect: Thousands of soldiers died on both sides without achieving anything; battles lasted for months on end.

5. The United States remained neutral for most of the war.

   Cause: Americans were divided on which side they supported; President Wilson did not want to involve the country in a European war.

   Effect: The American economy prospered by filling orders for war supplies; the United States continued trading with all nations.

B. Reviewing Key Terms

Directions: Briefly define each term.

6. nationalism pride in one's nation

7. militarism the policy of building up strong armed forces to prepare for war

8. terrorist one who uses threats and violence to promote a cause

9. kaiser the emperor of Germany

10. stalemate a deadlock in which neither side is strong enough to defeat the other

11. propaganda the spreading of ideas that help a cause or hurt an opposing cause

Name _____ Class _____ Date _____

Section 2 Guided Reading and Review
From Neutrality to War

A. As You Read

Directions: As you read Section 2 in your textbook, fill in supporting details for each main idea below: *Possible answers below*

Main Idea A: President Wilson tried to bring about peace.

1. Wilson tried to bring both sides together in peace talks.

2. Wilson kept the United States out of the war until 1918.

Main Idea B: The United States began preparations to enter the war.

3. Wilson lobbied for a stronger army and navy.

4. The United States broke off diplomatic relations with Germany.

5. Americans were outraged over Germany's attempt to draw Mexico into an alliance against the United States.

6. The United States supported the Russian revolutionaries who overthrew and killed the czar.

Main Idea C: Americans on the home front responded to the war effort.

7. Government agencies oversaw the war effort.

8. Movie stars helped sell Liberty Bonds to raise the money the United States needed for the war.

9. Many women took jobs to replace the men who joined the armed forces.

B. Reviewing Key Terms

Directions: Match each term with its definition.

Column I

_d_ 10. warmonger

_b_ 11. czar

_a_ 12. draft

_c_ 13. illiterate

_e_ 14. bureaucracy

_f_ 15. pacifist

Column II

a. law requiring people of a certain age to serve in the military

b. emperor of Russia

c. unable to read or write

d. person who tries to stir up war

e. a system of managing government through departments run by appointed officials

f. one who refuses to fight because of a belief that violence is wrong

CHAPTER 24

Section 3 Guided Reading and Review
Americans in Battle

A. As You Read

Directions: As you read Section 3 in your textbook, answer the following questions:
Possible answers below

1. Why did Russia withdraw from the war? The Bolshevik political party wanted to stage a

   communist revolution; Lenin argued that the war benefited only the ruling class.

2. What was the result of the Treaty of Brest-Litovsk? Russia gave up large amounts of land to

   Germany in exchange for peace; the Allies believed that Russia had betrayed them; Germany was able to move all its

   forces to the Western Front.

3. What was the battle at Amiens like? Thousands of German cannons fired on a small British force.

   Fighting continued for two weeks until the Germans retreated.

4. What did the United States Marines do at Belleau Wood? They won a bloody three-week

   battle against a more-experienced German army.

5. What happened at the Battle of the Argonne Forest? After weeks of fighting, a huge

   American force broke through the German defenses and won the battle.

6. How did the war end? The German government surrendered to the United States.

7. What were the costs of the war? Millions of soldiers died; many European cities and towns, especially

   in France, were destroyed; millions of survivors were left homeless and starving.

B. Reviewing Key Terms

Directions: Briefly explain the importance of each place to the Great War.

8. Amiens   site of the German "peace offensive," what they hoped would be the final battle against the Allies

9. Belleau Wood   site of battle between the United States Marines and the Germans; victory for the United States

10. the Argonne Forest   site of last major battle of war, between the Allies and Germany; Allies finally won battle

CHAPTER

24 Section 4 Guided Reading and Review

The Failed Peace

A. As You Read

Directions: As you read Section 4 in your textbook, complete each sentence.
Possible answers below

1. Wilson's goals after the war were to create a just and lasting peace rather than to take revenge on

   Germany, and to get European nations to agree to the Fourteen Points that would guarantee world peace.

2. The purpose of the League of Nations was to protect the independence of all nations so that

   they could live on equal terms of liberty and safety.

3. The Treaty of Versailles stated that Germany must take full blame for the war, pay

   reparations to the Allies, reduce the size of its military, return Alsace-Lorraine to France, and give up its

   overseas colonies.

4. Americans reacted to the Versailles Treaty in the following way: Most supported it, but

   some thought it was too hard on Germany; some isolationists opposed the League of Nations.

5. The League of Nations failed because the Senate rejection of the Treaty of Versailles meant that

   the United States did not join the League.

B. Reviewing Key Terms

Directions: Briefly define each term below.

6. Fourteen Points President Wilson's attempt to guarantee a just and lasting peace; included a call for a League of Nations, an end to secret agreements, freedom on the seas, free trade, arms limits.

7. League of Nations a proposed organization of nations whose job was to protect the independence of all nations

8. Peace of Paris five separate peace treaties that would set terms at the end of the war, including the Treaty of Versailles

9. Big Four the Allied nations of Italy, France, Britain, and the United States

10. Treaty of Versailles peace treaty between Germany and the Allies

CHAPTER

25 Section 1 Guided Reading and Review
Politics and Prosperity

A. As You Read

Directions: As you read Section 1 in your textbook, answer the following questions:
Possible answers below

1. Why did the Democrats lose the White House in 1920? Woodrow Wilson was no longer

   popular; a recession followed World War I, and the Democrats were blamed.

2. Why were the 1920 Cabinet members called the "Ohio Gang"? Most of them were

   Harding's friends from Ohio who took advantage of their government jobs.

3. What was the Teapot Dome scandal? The Secretary of the Interior illegally leased government land

   to oil executives.

4. What were the domestic presidential policies in the 1920s? Pro-business; they cut

   regulations on businesses and put businessmen in charge of government agencies.

5. What were the sources of the economic boom of the 1920s? Government's pro-business
   policies made investors confident enough to buy more stocks; this meant a rapid rise in the stock market.
   Installment buying also led to more spending.

6. How were relations between the United States and Latin America characterized

   during this period? American trade with and investment in Latin America increased. A potential war with

   Mexico was resolved diplomatically.

7. What type of government was in place in the Soviet Union? a communist government

   that did away with private property and attacked religion

8. What happened at the Washington Conference of 1921? The United States, Britain, and

   Japan agreed to limit the size of their navies.

B. Reviewing Key Terms

Directions: Identify each person listed.

9. Warren G. Harding Republican; elected president in 1920; pro-business; died in office of heart attack

10. Andrew Mellon Harding's Secretary of the Treasury; balanced the budget and lowered taxes

11. Herbert Hoover Harding's Secretary of Commerce; organized food supplies for Belgium during WWI; helped
    American business expand overseas

12. Albert Fall Harding's Secretary of the Interior; illegally leased government land to oil executives; sent to jail

13. Calvin Coolidge Harding's Vice President; became President when Harding died in office; pro-business

14. Dwight Morrow diplomat whom Coolidge sent to smooth over tensions with Mexico

15. V. I. Lenin ruler of the Soviet Union who created the world's first communist state

16. Jane Addams founder of the Women's International League for Peace and Freedom

CHAPTER

25

Section 2 Guided Reading and Review

New Ways of Life

A. As You Read

Directions: As you read Section 2 in your textbook, complete the chart by describing the social changes in each category. *Possible answers below*

1. Prohibition	The manufacture, sale, and transportation of liquor was banned in the United States. People began manufacturing their own liquor in stills at home, smuggling it in from abroad, or buying it in speak-easies. An entire new system of organized crime was born. Because Prohibition undermined respect for the law, it was repealed.
2. Women's Rights	Women won the right to vote in 1920. Soon, some women were chosen as delegates and elected to political office. Ready-made clothing freed many women from making their own. Electric appliances meant less time was needed for housework. Many women began working outside the home during and after World War I.
3. Transportation	A tremendous rise in automobile sales meant that people could live farther from their workplaces. This gave rise to suburbs. More and more roads were paved, and more highways were built. There was a great increase in the number of filling stations. Travel became easier and more frequent.

B. Reviewing Key Terms

Directions: Use each term correctly in a sentence about the Roaring Twenties.
Possible answers below

4. Prohibition The era of Prohibition, during which alcoholic beverages could not be sold, gave rise to a network of organized criminals.

5. bootleggers "Bootleggers" got their name from the smuggled bottles of liquor they sometimes hid in their boots.

6. repeal Congress realized by the end of the 1920s that it was necessary to repeal Prohibition, a law many Americans flouted daily.

7. League of Women Voters Carrie Chapman Catt founded the League of Women Voters, which worked to educate voters and fight for women's rights.

8. Equal Rights Amendment The Equal Rights Amendment, which would forbid any gender-based discrimination, has never been ratified.

9. suburb A suburb is a community outside a city.

CHAPTER

25

Section 3 Guided Reading and Review

The Roaring Twenties

A. As You Read

Directions: As you read Section 3 in your textbook, fill in the chart with examples of 1920s crazes, innovations, artists, and celebrities. *Possible answers below*

1. Dances	Charleston, Lindy Hop, Shimmy
2. Fashions	short skirts, bobbed hair, bright red lipstick
3. Music	jazz
4. Literature	realistic novels by Ernest Hemingway, F. Scott Fitzgerald, Sinclair Lewis; poetry by Edna St. Vincent Millay; realistic plays by Eugene O'Neill; poetry and stories by African Americans from the "Harlem Renaissance," including Langston Hughes
5. Celebrities	Charles Lindbergh, who flew solo across the Atlantic Ocean; sports figures such as boxer Jack Dempsey and baseball player Babe Ruth

B. Reviewing Key Terms

Directions: Match each person with his or her description.

Column I

  _f_   6. Louis Armstrong

  _g_   7. Bessie Smith

  _i_   8. Ernest Hemingway

  _h_   9. Sinclair Lewis

  _c_   10. Eugene O'Neill

  _e_   11. Langston Hughes

  _d_   12. Zora Neale Hurston

  _a_   13. Babe Ruth

  _b_   14. Charles Lindbergh

Column II

a. hit 60 home runs in one season; record stood for over 30 years

b. flew solo across the Atlantic Ocean

c. playwright; wrote realistic dramas

d. writer and collector of African American folktales

e. poet; wrote "The Negro Speaks of Rivers"

f. trumpeter who helped create jazz music

g. jazz singer

h. author of *Babbit* and *Main Street*

i. author of *The Sun Also Rises* and *A Farewell to Arms*

Guided Reading and Review

CHAPTER

25

Section 4 Guided Reading and Review

A Nation Divided

A. As You Read

Directions: As you read Section 4 in your textbook, fill in supporting details under each main idea below: *Possible answers below*

Main Idea A: Many Americans did not share in the boom of the 1920s.

1. Social and technological changes led to the loss of thousands of jobs in mining and in the railroad and garment industries.

2. European farmers no longer needed American farm products after the war ended.

3. Workers often went on strike for higher wages.

4. The courts and the government continually sided with management against labor.

Main Idea B: Communism's rise in the East made Americans fear a communist revolution in the West.

5. The American government took harsh action against many foreign-born anarchists.

6. Sacco and Vanzetti were executed without a fair trial.

7. Congress devised immigration quotas that favored northern Europe and limited or banned immigration from Eastern Europe and Asia.

B. Reviewing Key Terms

Directions: Briefly define each term.

8. company union — labor organization controlled by management

9. sabotage — secret destruction of property or interference with work in factories

10. anarchist — one who opposes organized government

11. deport — expel from a country

12. nativism — anti-foreign feeling

13. quota system — system allowing only a certain number of people from each country to enter the United States

---

Guided Reading and Review

Name _____ Class _____ Date _____

26 Section 1 Guided Reading and Review
The Great Crash

A. As You Read

Directions: As you read Section 1 in your textbook, list one cause and one effect for each of the following: *Possible answers below*

1. Farmers' incomes fell during the 1920s.

   Cause: *Expenses rose faster than prices; farmers did not reduce production.*

   Effect: *Farmers could not pay off their loans, which weakened the banking system.*

2. The stock market crashed on October 29, 1929.

   Cause: *Investors noticed the economy slowing down and began selling stocks; many people were forced to sell in order to repay loans.*

   Effect: *Many people lost everything they had; Americans lost confidence in the economy; businesses laid off many workers.*

3. The banking system was weakened.

   Cause: *Many people and businesses could not repay loans made during the 1920s.*

   Effect: *Many banks had to close; people with bank accounts lost all their money.*

4. Factories cut back on production.

   Cause: *People had no money, so there was much less demand for the goods factories produced.*

   Effect: *Factory owners cut wages and laid off workers.*

5. Most Americans blamed President Hoover for the Great Depression.

   Cause: *Hoover was President when the market crashed; he was unable to lead the country out of the depression.*

   Effect: *Voters did not reelect Hoover.*

B. Reviewing Key Terms

Directions: Complete each sentence by writing the correct term in the blank.

6. Many investors could not repay loans from stocks purchased _____*on margin*_____.

7. October 29, 1929, the date of the stock market crash, is called _____*Black Tuesday*_____.

8. People or businesses unable to pay their debts are described as _____*bankrupt*_____.

9. Groups of shacks in which homeless people lived during the depression were called _____*Hoovervilles*_____ because people blamed the President for the depression.

10. In 1932, the _____*Bonus Army*_____ marched to Washington to demand immediate payment of money not due to be paid until 1945.

CHAPTER

26 Section 2 Guided Reading and Review

FDR and the New Deal

A. As You Read

Directions: As you read Section 2 in your textbook, complete the chart below by writing key steps the government took to achieve each main goal of the New Deal.

Possible answers below

Goal A: to provide relief for the unemployed

1. established government programs that hired thousands of workers

2. established the FERA to distribute money to the unemployed

Goal B: to plan the economic recovery

3. forced industry to establish production codes

4. Industries hired workers for public works projects.

5. paid farmers not to grow certain crops of which there was a surplus

6. extended electric service into rural areas not previously served

7. remade the Tennessee River Valley

Goal C: to prevent another depression

8. passed laws to regulate the stock market

9. passed laws to regulate the banking system

B. Reviewing Key Terms

Directions: Briefly describe each New Deal program, and mark each A, B, or C to identify which of the above goals it helped achieve.

10. Civilian Conservation Corps A; hired unemployed young men to plant trees, build bridges, and work on

    other conservation and projects

11. Works Progress Administration A; the government sponsored construction and arts projects and

    paid builders, actors, writers, and others to take part

12. National Industrial Recovery Act B; each industry wrote a production code for itself that was meant

    to end price-cutting and worker layoffs

13. Public Works Administration B; hired workers for thousands of public works projects such as Grand

    Coulee Dam

14. Agricultural Adjustment Act B; paid farmers not to grow certain crops, assuming that small harvests

    would bring prices back up

Name _____ Class _____ Date _____

CHAPTER

26 Section 3 Guided Reading and Review

Response to the New Deal

A. As You Read

Directions: As you read Section 3 in your textbook, list three ways in which the New Deal changed the United States government. Then, fill in the chart with arguments for and against these changes. *Possible answers below*

1. The government hired thousands of people who were not civil servants. _____

2. The government began regulating industry and agriculture. _____

3. The government played a huge role in people's lives, instead of the small role that it had traditionally played.

For	Against
4. New Deal legislation ended the banking crisis, protected farmers, and provided work for the millions of unemployed. The government fulfilled its responsibility to help all citizens. The New Deal had saved the nation's democratic system, restoring the nation's economic health while preserving its liberties.	5. The New Deal interfered in people's lives, threatening both individual freedoms and private property. It gave the government too much power. The government was spending more than it took in. The New Deal did not end the depression.

B. Reviewing Key Terms

Directions: Briefly define each term.

6. pension   a sum of money paid regularly to a person after retirement _____

7. collective bargaining   the process by which a union negotiates with management for a contract _____

8. sit-down strike   occurs when workers stop running machines and refuse to leave the workplace _____

9. deficit spending   spending more than one takes in _____

10. national debt   total sum of money the government owes _____

Guided Reading and Review

CHAPTER

26  Section 4 Guided Reading and Review

The Nation in Hard Times

A. As You Read

Directions: As you read Section 4 in your textbook, answer the following questions:

Possible answers below

1. What caused the dust storms that swept the Great Plains during the 1930s?

   Years of overgrazing by cattle and plowing had removed the grasses that held the topsoil in place. Drought dried the

   soil out, and high winds did the rest.

2. Why did farmers from the Great Plains pack up and migrate to California?

   Dust storms and drought made it impossible to farm the land. Farmers hoped to get work on farms and orchards

   in California.

3. How did Eleanor Roosevelt change the job of First Lady? _She toured the nation, speaking_

   publicly on the issues. She wrote a newspaper column. She took strong positions on social issues.

4. What special struggles did ethnic minorities face during the depression? _It was harder_

   than ever for them to find jobs. Many Mexicans were deported. Many Asians faced violence.

5. What did movies contribute to society during the depression? _They provided a temporary_

   escape for people who were struggling to survive. They worked to restore Americans' faith in the future.

B. Reviewing Key Terms

Directions: Briefly identify each artist's contribution to the depression.

6. John Steinbeck   _author of The Grapes of Wrath, novel about the Okies' migration to California_

7. Thomas Hart Benton   _painter of murals showing the history of the frontier_

8. Dorothea Lange   _photographer of sufferings of Dust Bowl farm families_

9. Orson Welles   _actor and presenter of The War of the Worlds, which convinced listeners that an actual invasion_

   from Mars was taking place

Name _____ Class _____ Date _____

Section 1 Guided Reading and Review
The Gathering Storm

A. As You Read

Directions: As you read Section 1 in your textbook, fill in the graphic organizer with details of each country's government on the eve of World War II.   *Possible answers below*

Soviet Union	1.	communist government headed by Joseph Stalin; totalitarian state with Stalin as dictator; peasants ordered to hand their land and animals over to the state; people forced to work in labor camps; millions executed for alleged political offenses
Italy	2.	fascist government headed by Benito Mussolini; all other political parties outlawed; program of military aggression; successful invasion of Ethiopia in 1935
Germany	3.	Nazi government headed by Adolf Hitler; totalitarian state with Hitler as dictator; government controlled all aspects of German society; government-sponsored persecution of Jews; began to work toward expansion of the German border; message of revenge for Treaty of Versailles
Japan	4.	military state; message of racial hatred toward other Asians and non-Asians; successful invasion of Manchuria

B. Reviewing Key Terms

Directions: Briefly define each term, and note which country or countries it is associated with: use S for the Soviet Union, I for Italy, G for Germany, or J for Japan.

5. totalitarian state   state in which one party controls government and every aspect of people's lives; S, I, G

_____

_____

6. fascism   governmental system rooted in militarism, extreme nationalism, and blind loyalty to the state; I, G

_____

_____

7. Nazis   short for "National Socialist German Workers' Party"; G

_____

_____

8. concentration camp   prison camp for civilians who were considered enemies of the state; G

_____

_____

Name _____ Class _____ Date _____

Section 2 Guided Reading and Review
World War II Begins

A. As You Read

Directions: As you read Section 2 in your textbook, number the events below in chronological order. List one effect of each event.

___6___ 1. Japan bombs Pearl Harbor, Hawaii.

Effect: The United States declares war on Japan.

___3___ 2. Hitler and Stalin agree to divide Eastern Europe between their nations.

Effect: Germany invades and annexes Poland while the Soviets invade eastern Poland and annex Latvia, Lithuania, and Estonia.

___4___ 3. The German army invades France.

Effect: Italy also attacks France; Britain joins the fighting on the French side; France falls to Germany in six weeks.

___2___ 4. Germany invades and annexes Austria.

Effect: Hitler grows more confident when he is unchallenged and soon annexes the Sudetenland (western Czechoslovakia).

___1___ 5. Japan declares all-out war on China and begins bombing major cities.

Effect: The United States is alarmed at Japanese undermining of Open Door Policy and the threat to the Philippines.

___5___ 6. The United States Congress passes the Lend-Lease Act.

Effect: The United States begins sending equipment and supplies to Britain.

B. Reviewing Key Terms

Directions: Briefly define or identify each term.

7. Munich Conference — Meeting in German city of Munich among leaders of France, Britain, Germany, and Italy; after seizing Sudetenland, Hitler promises no further annexation.

8. appeasement — Giving in to aggression in order to avoid war; France and Britain appeased Germany at the Munich Conference.

9. blitzkrieg — German term meaning "lightning war"; description of Hitler's invasion of Poland

10. Axis — name given to Germany, Italy, Japan, and six other nations fighting the Allied powers

11. Allies — name given to Britain, France, the Soviet Union, the United States, China, and 45 other nations fighting the Axis powers

12. Atlantic Charter — British-American document stating that Allies sought no new territory from war, that Allies would support universal self-determination, and after the war create a system of general security.

Name _____ Class _____ Date _____

Section 3 Guided Reading and Review

Americans in Wartime

A. As You Read

Directions: As you read Section 3 in your textbook, answer the following questions:
Possible answers below

1. What did women do in the armed forces during the war? They flew planes ferrying bombers from base to base and towing targets. They served near the front lines in all branches of the armed forces, although they were not allowed in combat.

2. Why were American consumer goods rationed during the war? Fewer consumer goods were being produced because more war supplies were being produced.

3. Why did America's entrance into the war have the effect that it did on the economy? Entrance into the war made the economy boom because suddenly there was a huge demand for workers. The armed services also employed thousands of people.

4. What kinds of changes did the war bring for women on the home front? Women took many jobs traditionally held by men. Equal pay for men and women was established; women's fashions changed.

5. What caused the race riots in American cities in the 1940s? Black employment increased, and as black and white Americans worked together, racial tension also increased. Competition for housing in cities increased tension.

6. What was the African American experience in the military? The military was segregated. African American units served heroically in all branches of the service under the command of white officers.

7. What happened to Japanese Americans during the war? Many were forced to leave their homes and live in "relocation camps" because people were concerned that they might be loyal to Japan, an enemy nation. Many Japanese Americans served with distinction in the military.

B. Reviewing Key Terms

Directions: Use each term correctly in a sentence about the homefront during World War II. Possible answers below

8. War Production Board   The War Production Board oversaw the conversion of factory production from consumer goods to guns, ships, aircraft, and other war materials.

9. victory garden   Because fresh produce was rationed, Americans grew vegetables in their own "victory gardens."

10. Rosie the Riveter   "Rosie the Riveter," a Norman Rockwell illustration, symbolized American women's contribution to the war effort.

11. "Double V" Campaign   The two "V"s of the "Double V" Campaign were victories over the enemy abroad and over discrimination at home.

12. Tuskegee Airmen   The Tuskegee Airmen were African American fighter pilots who destroyed or damaged about 400 enemy aircraft.

Name _____ Class _____ Date _____

Section 4 Guided Reading and Review
The Allies Turn the Tide

A. As You Read

Directions: As you read Section 4 in your textbook, list the main events that happened to each country between 1942 and 1945.

1. Soviet Union

   resisted German invasion; more than 1 million Russians died in siege of Leningrad; urged establishment of Second

   Front in France; pushed Germans out of Soviet Union in 1943; eventually lost 9 million soldiers in war

2. Japan

   seized American possessions in the Pacific; forced MacArthur to withdraw American forces there; lost the Battle of

   Midway to the United States

3. United States

   fought with Japan in the Pacific; lost at Bataan but won decisively at Midway; landed at Normandy in France and

   marched on Paris; liberated Paris from Nazi rule in August 1944; bombed German cities; FDR died in 1944,

   replaced by Vice President Truman

4. Germany

   invaded Soviet Union; laid siege to Leningrad for over two years; surrendered to United States in North Africa; lost

   Paris to Allied forces; lost Battle of the Bulge; cities bombed by Allied planes; Hitler committed suicide during

   bombing of Berlin; surrendered to Allies in 1945

B. Reviewing Key Terms

Directions: Briefly define or identify each term.

5. Battle of Midway   battle in Pacific between Japan and United States; decisive victory for Allies

6. Operation Overlord   name given to the Allied invasion of Europe that took place in June 1944

7. D-Day   June 6, 1944; the day the Allies landed in Normandy and began marching to Paris

8. Battle of the Bulge   Battle between German and Allied forces; Germans slowed the Allied march to Berlin but did not stop it.

CHAPTER

27

Section 5 Guided Reading and Review
The End of the War

A. As You Read

Directions: As you read Section 5 in your textbook, fill in supporting details under each main idea. *Possible answers below*

Main Idea A: One goal of the United States was to regain the Philippines.

1. <u>Americans captured one Japanese-held island after another in a system of island hopping.</u>

2. <u>Navajo soldiers sent messages in their own language; the Japanese could never break this code.</u>

Main Idea B: A second goal of the United States was to invade Japan.

3. <u>The United States attacked Japan with conventional weapons and atomic bombs.</u>

Main Idea C: Japan surrendered in 1945.

4. <u>After the atomic bombs were dropped, the emperor of Japan announced Japan's surrender to the United States.</u>

Main Idea D: World War II was the deadliest war in history.

5. <u>Between 30 and 60 million people were killed during the war.</u>

6. <u>Bombers destroyed houses, factories, and farms, leaving many survivors homeless and with no way to make a living.</u>

7. <u>Prisoners of war were treated brutally, and many died.</u>

8. <u>Millions of Jews, Gypsies, Poles, and Slavs were massacred.</u>

B. Reviewing Key Terms

Directions: Fill in each blank with the correct term.

9. The Americans captured steppingstones to Japan in a strategy known as

   _____<u>island hopping</u>_____.

10. A _____<u>kamikaze</u>_____ pilot is one who uses his own plane as a missile, knowing

    that he will die when he hits his target.

11. The _____<u>Potsdam Declaration</u>_____ warned Japan to surrender or face destruction.

12. The deliberate massacre of millions of Jews, Poles, Gypsies, and Slavs is known as

    the _____<u>Holocaust</u>_____.

13. At the _____<u>Nuremberg Trials</u>_____, 12 Nazis were sentenced to death for war crimes, and

    thousands more were imprisoned.

Name _____ Class _____ Date _____

28 Section 1 Guided Reading and Review

The Cold War Begins

A. As You Read

Directions: As you read Section 1 in the textbook, list one cause and one effect of each of the following events:

1. After World War II, the Soviet Union's relationship with Britain and the United States was one of distrust.

   Cause: Each side thought the other had the wrong system of government; each feared a takeover by the other.

   Effect: The Cold War began and lasted nearly 50 years.

2. President Truman decided on a Cold War policy of containment.

   Cause: The United States wanted to stop the spread of communism.

   Effect: The United States helped Greece and Turkey withstand communist threats.

3. Secretary of State George Marshall urged passage of the Marshall Plan.

   Cause: Many nations needed economic help to recover from the devastation of World War II; the United States hoped that countries receiving aid would not become communist nations.

   Effect: The United States gave $12 billion in aid to Western European countries.

4. President Truman approved an airlift to West Berlin.

   Cause: Truman would not let Berlin fall into Soviet hands, but he did not want to send ground troops to Europe.

   Effect: Stalin realized that the West would not abandon West Berlin, and he lifted the blockade in 1949.

5. The East German government built the Berlin Wall.

   Cause: Too many East Germans were fleeing to West Berlin, embarrassing the Communists.

   Effect: Germans could no longer cross from one side of the city to the other. Contact between family and friends was cut off.

B. Reviewing Key Terms

Directions: Complete each sentence by writing the correct term in the blank.

6. The _____Cold War_____ was an intense rivalry and standoff between the forces of communism and democracy.

7. After World War II, many eastern European countries became _____satellite nations_____ of the Soviet Union.

8. The _____"iron curtain"_____ was an imaginary barrier between communist nations and democratically governed countries.

9. The _____Truman Doctrine_____ set out a program encouraging nations to resist communist expansion.

10. The _____United Nations_____, an international peacekeeping force, was the successor to the failed League of Nations.

Name _____ Class _____ Date _____

Section 2 Guided Reading and Review
The Korean War Period

A. As You Read
Directions: As you read Section 2 in the textbook, answer the following questions:

1. What was the immediate cause of the Korean War? <u>North Korean troops invaded South Korea</u>

<u>in June 1950.</u>

2. What was the UN response to the outbreak of fighting in Korea? <u>The UN agreed to a</u>

<u>request by the United States to send an army to Korea to fight on the side of the South Koreans.</u>

3. What happened at Inchon? <u>General MacArthur landed UN forces at Inchon, behind North Korean lines,</u>

<u>and forced the North Korean troops back across the 38th parallel.</u>

4. What role did China play in the Korean War? <u>China joined the war on the North Korean side.</u>

5. What was the source of the dispute between Truman and MacArthur? <u>MacArthur wanted</u>

<u>to attack China; Truman feared that this would cause a world war.</u>

6. What were the terms of the armistice between the two sides? <u>The border between North and</u>

<u>South Korea was established near the 38th parallel. A demilitarized zone was established on either side of this border.</u>

7. What effect did the Korean War have on Americans at home? <u>It made them more worried</u>

<u>about Communists at home.</u>

8. How and why did Joseph McCarthy become notorious? <u>McCarthy capitalized on American</u>
<u>anticommunist feeling to accuse many people of communism. He was never able to prove his claims and was eventually</u>
<u>censured by the Senate.</u>

B. Reviewing Key Terms
Directions: Match each term with its definition.

Column I	Column II
<u>c</u> 9. 38th parallel	a. officially condemn
<u>d</u> 10. demilitarized zone	b. lying under oath
<u>b</u> 11. perjury	c. line of latitude along which Korea was temporarily divided
<u>a</u> 12. censure	d. an area with no military forces

CHAPTER

28 Section 3 Guided Reading and Review
Regional Conflicts

A. As You Read

Directions: As you read Section 3 in the textbook, describe the effects of the Cold War in each region or country. *Possible answers below*

1. Africa

    Effects: Many nations that had been colonies won their independence. Civil and border wars resulted. The United States and the Soviet Union backed various countries, searching for allies. Therefore, local wars became international incidents. The Cold War intensified a civil war in Angola.

2. Asia

    Effects: India won independence from Britain and was partitioned into India and Pakistan. The United States and the Soviet Union tried to form alliances with both nations. In Indochina, separate nationalist groups fought for nearly 30 years for supremacy and independence.

3. Cuba

    Effects: In 1959, a revolution put Fidel Castro and a communist government in power. The United States was nervous about having a Soviet ally 90 miles off its coast. In the 1961 Bay of Pigs invasion, the United States failed to overthrow the Castro regime. In 1962, the United States discovered that Soviets were building missile bases on Cuba, bringing the world to the brink of nuclear war; President Kennedy and Soviet leader Khrushchev resolved the standoff peacefully.

4. Latin America

    Effects: Latin American countries were attracted to the philosophy behind communism. To persuade them to remain friendly to the United States, President Kennedy launched many economic aid programs. Whenever fighting broke out in Latin America, the United States supported the anticommunist side in the fighting.

B. Reviewing Key Terms

Directions: Briefly describe the purpose of each organization.

5. Alliance for Progress   aid program through which the United States would build schools and hospitals and improve farming and sanitation in exchange for a country's passing political reforms

6. Peace Corps   group of volunteers who worked in developing countries for two-year terms as teachers, engineers, and technical advisers

7. Organization of American States   promoted economic progress in the Americas by investing in transportation and industry

8. National Aeronautics and Space Administration   directed an American space program to compete with that of the Soviets

CHAPTER

28 Section 4 Guided Reading and Review
The War in Vietnam

A. As You Read

Dirctions: As you read Section 4 in the textbook, answer the following questions:
Possible answers below

1. What were the results of the peace conference after Ho Chi Minh defeated the

    French in Vietnam? <u>Vietnam was divided into communist North Vietnam and noncommunist South Vietnam.</u>

    _____

    _____

2. Who were the Vietcong? <u>They were South Vietnamese peasants discontented with the government. They</u>

    <u>became guerrilla rebels supported by North Vietnam.</u>

    _____

3. Why did the United States become involved in Vietnam? <u>The United States did not want</u>

    <u>South Vietnam to be taken over by a communist government.</u>

    _____

4. What did the Gulf of Tonkin Resolution state? <u>that President Johnson, as commander in chief,</u>

    <u>was entitled to take all necessary measures to defend against an attack or prevent armed aggression in Vietnam</u>

    _____

5. How did Americans at home feel about the Vietnam War? <u>Support for the war faded quickly,</u>

    <u>as a result of the television coverage of the battles and the inequalities of the military draft.</u>

    _____

6. Why was the Tet Offensive a turning point in the war? <u>The Vietcong won a major political</u>

    <u>victory by showing that no part of Vietnam was safe from a Vietcong attack.</u>

    _____

7. What effect did the Vietnam War have in Cambodia? <u>Nixon ordered bombing of communist</u>

    <u>bases in Cambodia, touching off a civil war followed by a reign of terror by the victorious Cambodian communist</u>

    <u>Khmer Rouge forces.</u>

B. Reviewing Key Terms   Possible answers below

Directions: Briefly describe each person's role in the Vietnam War.

8. Ho Chi Minh <u>Communist leader of Vietnamese nationalists; led the successful rebellion against French rule; became leader of North Vietnam</u>

9. Lyndon Johnson <u>American President who first sent troops to Vietnam; did not seek reelection when he saw how unpopular the war had become and how impossible it would be to win</u>

10. Richard Nixon <u>bombed Cambodia, setting off a terrible civil war there; gradually withdrew American troops from Vietnam</u>

Guided Reading and Review

Name _____ Class _____ Date _____

A. As You Read

Directions: As you read Section 5 in the textbook, complete the following sentences:

1. Germans tore down _____the Berlin Wall_____ in 1989.

2. The United States had refused to recognize the Chinese communist government led by _____Mao Zedong_____.

3. President Nixon became the first American President since the beginning of the Cold War to visit _____the Soviet Union_____.

4. The Soviets and the Americans worked together on a policy of _____détente_____, which eased the tensions of foreign relations for both sides.

5. Soviet troops invaded _____Afghanistan_____ in 1979 in support of the communist government that had just seized power there.

6. _____Ronald Reagan_____ took office in 1981, firmly believing that the Soviet Union was the focus of evil in the modern world.

7. Soviet leader _____Mikhail Gorbachev_____ instituted sweeping reforms to help his country solve its vast economic and social problems.

8. In Poland, labor leader _____Lech Walesa_____ led the fight against the communists and later became the freely elected head of the government.

B. Reviewing Key Terms

Directions: Use each term correctly in a statement about the end of the Cold War.
Possible answers below

9. SALT agreement The SALT agreement between the superpowers stated that they would limit their arsenals of nuclear warheads and missiles.

10. Star Wars "Star Wars" was the nickname of a Reagan program, never implemented, to develop weapons that would destroy Soviet missiles in space.

11. Solidarity Solidarity was the name of the Polish labor union that fought for labor reforms.

12. glasnost Glasnost was a policy of openness that replaced the Soviet tradition of silencing any criticism of the government.

Name _____ Class _____ Date _____

 Section 1 Guided Reading and Review

Postwar Politics and Prosperity

A. As You Read

Directions: As you read Section 1 in the textbook, give one cause and one effect for each statement.

1. During World War II, Congress passed the GI Bill of Rights.

   Cause: The government wanted to help returning veterans readjust to civilian life.

   Effect: Thousands of veterans were able to buy homes, go to college, or start businesses.

2. President Truman was reelected in 1948.

   Cause: Truman traveled the country, speaking directly to the voters.

   Effect: Truman proposed New Deal-style reforms called the Fair Deal.

3. In the 1940s and 1950s, the American population grew by many millions.

   Cause: Victory in the war and the prosperity of the country gave Americans the confidence to start families.

   Effect: A need arose for more schools and hospitals and new housing.

4. Suburban communities of identical houses and shopping malls became common.

   Cause: The GI Bill encouraged veterans to buy their own homes in the suburbs.

   Effect: Cities began to look run-down and deserted.

5. The federal government built thousands of miles of highways.

   Cause: Nine of ten families in the suburbs owned cars by the 1960s.

   Effect: The highway system contributed to a boom in the trucking and automobile industries; Americans could travel more easily; motels and fast-food restaurants sprang up along the highways.

6. Television became a major source of news and entertainment.

   Cause: TV sets were cheap and provided free entertainment in the home.

   Effect: People stayed home more often instead of going out for entertainment.

B. Reviewing Key Terms

Directions: Use each term correctly in an accurate statement about postwar America.
Possible answers below

7. inflation Because wartime government control of prices ended with the war, inflation occurred, raising prices.

8. baby boom During the baby boom of the 1940s and 1950s, the American population grew by about 50 million.

9. standard of living A suburban house, a car in the garage, two or three children, and a television set all were signs of a high postwar standard of living.

10. beatnik Beatniks were, in the words of Jack Kerouac, "wear[y] with all forms of the modern industrial state."

Name _____ Class _____ Date _____

Section 2 Guided Reading and Review
The Civil Rights Movement

A. As You Read
Directions: As you read Section 2 in the textbook, explain the importance of each of the following to the civil rights movement: *Possible answers below*

1. NAACP _National Association for the Advancement of Colored People; helped African Americans protest for_ _their rights by providing financial and legal assistance_

2. Brooklyn Dodgers _Major League Baseball team that hired Jackie Robinson, the first African American_ _player in the major leagues since the 1880s_

3. *Brown* v. *Board of Education of Topeka* _Supreme Court case in which an African American sued for_ _his daughter's right to attend the nearby all-white school; Thurgood Marshall won the case for the plaintiff, and_ _thereafter, schools were integrated._

4. *Hernández* v. *Texas* _Supreme Court case in which Mexicans won the right to sit on juries in Texas_

5. Montgomery Improvement Association (MIA) _Organization formed by African Americans to_ _support Rosa Parks, who had refused to give up her bus seat to a white passenger; the MIA appointed Martin Luther King, Jr., to lead the bus boycott and to speak for the civil rights movement._

6. Southern Christian Leadership Conference _Organization formed by King and other African_ _American southern leaders after the bus boycott case was won; its purpose was to carry on the crusade for civil rights._

B. Reviewing Key Terms
Directions: Briefly define each term.

7. segregation _strict separation of races_

8. integration _mixing of different racial groups_

9. civil rights movement _widespread protest against segregation and other discriminatory customs_

10. boycott _refusal to use or purchase goods or services; specifically, refusal to travel on Montgomery city buses_

11. civil disobedience _nonviolent protests against unjust laws_

Name _____ Class _____ Date _____

Section 3 Guided Reading and Review

Protest, Reform, and Doubt

A. As You Read

Directions: As you read Section 3 in the textbook, correct each of the following false statements:

1. Americans were concerned that presidential candidate Richard Nixon might be more loyal to the Catholic Church than to the country. _replace Nixon with John F. Kennedy_

   _____

2. Lee Harvey Oswald became President after John F. Kennedy was assassinated.

   replace Oswald with Lyndon B. Johnson

3. The Warren Commission ordered that Lee Harvey Oswald be executed for killing the President. _The Warren Commission decided that Oswald murdered the President on his own._

4. Lyndon B. Johnson's Great Society programs took money from the poor and gave it to the wealthy. _The Great Society used taxes to pay for programs that helped raise the standard of living for the poor._

5. The counterculture movement arose as a result of protests against the Vietnam War.

   The counterculture movement was a response to and a protest against mainstream American culture of the 1950s.

6. In the 1968 presidential election, Richard Nixon defeated Robert F. Kennedy.

   replace Kennedy with Hubert Humphrey and George Wallace

7. Nixon is best remembered for his economic policies. _Nixon is best remembered for his_

   involvement in Watergate and his resignation from the presidency.

B. Reviewing Key Terms

Directions: Match each President with the description of his term of office.

Column I

_b_ 8. John F. Kennedy

_e_ 9. Lyndon B. Johnson

_c_ 10. Richard M. Nixon

_d_ 11. Gerald R. Ford

_a_ 12. Jimmy Carter

Column II

a. high inflation; strong support for human rights

b. created Peace Corps; began space program; assassinated in third year of his term

c. covered up his connection to burglary of Democratic national headquarters; resigned presidency under threat of impeachment

d. pardon of Nixon lost him much public support

e. goal was for all Americans to achieve decent standard of living; created numerous social programs such as Head Start

CHAPTER
29

Section 4 Guided Reading and Review

The Crusade for Equal Rights

A. As You Read

Directions: As you read Section 4 in the textbook, identify and briefly describe the various methods people used to protest during the civil rights movement.
Possible answers below

1. nonviolent direct action; included sit-ins, boycotts, marches, and other peaceful methods of protest

2. "black power" movement; included push for economic independence, violent protests, participation in race riots

3. legislation; included federal civil rights laws such as Voting Rights Act and Civil Rights Act

B. Reviewing Key Terms

Directions: Briefly identify or describe the importance of each of the following:

4. Greensboro, North Carolina location of the first sit-in

5. Congress of Racial Equality youth group that organized busloads of riders who rode from town to town to integrate bus terminals in the South

6. Voting Rights Act legislation that allowed federal officials to register voters in states practicing discrimination; ended literacy tests used to block African Americans from voting

7. Black Panthers radical group that preached that African Americans must arm themselves and fight for their rights

8. Malcolm X Black Muslim who initially preached that African Americans should separate themselves from white society

9. Watts, Los Angeles, California site of race riots of 1965 in which thousands were arrested and many injured or killed

10. Thurgood Marshall former NAACP lawyer who became first African American Supreme Court justice; appointed to bench by Lyndon Johnson

CHAPTER

30 Section 1 Guided Reading and Review

The Conservative Revolt

A. As You Read

Directions: As you read Section 1 in the textbook, answer the following questions:
Possible answers below

1. Why did the country become more conservative as the century ended? _____

   Many people feared that the power and size of government had expanded too far.

2. What were the goals of conservative citizens and politicians? to cut social programs, to
   reduce regulations on big business, to lower taxes, to reduce the size of the federal government, to return society
   to traditional values, and to balance the federal budget

3. Why was Ronald Reagan called "the Great Communicator"? Reagan's background in acting

   and long experience in public speaking helped him present ideas in terms that everyone could understand.

4. What were Reagan's economic goals? to cut taxes so that people could spend more money, to cut

   federal spending to reduce the size of the government, and to reduce restrictions on big business

5. What were the problems in George H.W. Bush's presidency? Bush was unable to keep his
   promise not to raise taxes, a fact that angered conservatives. As taxes rose, the economy grew weaker, which hurt
   everyone. Banks failed, and businesses laid off employees.

6. What were the successes in Bill Clinton's presidency? The federal deficit began a steady

   decline; when Clinton left office, there was a budget surplus. Clinton also overhauled the welfare system.

7. What was unusual about the 2000 presidential election? Gore won the popular vote, but

   after the Supreme Court ruled to stop Florida recounts, Bush won the election.

B. Reviewing Key Terms

Directions: Briefly identify or define each term.

8. Moral Majority Founded by evangelical leader Jerry Falwell, this group aided political candidates who

   favored conservative religious goals.

9. Reaganomics nickname for Ronald Reagan's economic policies: cutting taxes, cutting spending on social

   programs, and deregulating businesses

10. deregulation reduction of restrictions on businesses

   _____

11. Contract with America legislative package promoted by Republicans in the House of Representatives;

   included trimming social welfare programs, reducing environmental regulations, and slashing taxes

Guided Reading and Review

Name _____ Class _____ Date _____

30  Section 2 Guided Reading and Review

American Leadership in a New World

A. As You Read

Directions: As you read Section 2 in the textbook, complete the following sentences:

1. The United States became the world's only superpower when _the Soviet Union broke apart_ _in 1991._

2. Filipino protest against dictator Marcos resulted in _the election of Corazon Aquino and a_ _democracy in the Philippines._

3. China responded to a people's campaign for democratic reforms by _sending the army to_ _crush the demonstrations; many people were arrested or killed._

4. The United States and Russia continued to work together to _reduce the number of nuclear_ _arms in the world._

5. The Comprehensive Test Ban Treaty failed because _China and Russia ignored it, and the_ _United States Congress refused to approve it._

B. Reviewing Key Terms

Directions: Match each term with its definition.

Column I

___b___ 6. apartheid

___d___ 7. sanctions

___c___ 8. global democracy

___a___ 9. arms race

Column II

a. competition to have the most weapons

b. strict separation of races

c. establishment of freely elected governments all over the world

d. measures designed to make a country change its policies

CHAPTER

30  Section 3 Guided Reading and Review

The Spread of Regional Conflict

A. As You Read

Directions: As you read Section 3 in the textbook, fill in details about each regional conflict. For those conflicts not directly involving the United States, include a brief description of the role the United States has played in each conflict. *Possible answers below*

Arab-Israeli Conflict

1. After World War II, a Jewish state was established in Palestine. Arabs in the area objected. In several brief wars, Israel defeated its Arab neighbors. Palestinian Arabs continued to wage guerrilla warfare against Israel. The United States strongly supported Israel but tried to broker peace between the warring factions.

Iran and Iraq

2. An anti-American government came to power in Iran in 1979. When the United States allowed the former Shah of Iran to enter the country for medical treatment, Iran seized the American embassy and held 53 people hostage for over a year. In 1990, the United States went to war with Iraq over its invasion of Kuwait, an important American trade partner.

Terrorism and the United States

3. Because of anger over American politics and culture, some radical Muslim groups have sponsored terrorist attacks against the United States. These attacks have taken place both overseas and in the United States itself. Most notable were the attacks that took place on September 11, 2001.

B. Reviewing Key Terms

Directions: Briefly identify each term. Note to which of the above conflicts it is most relevant.

4. OPEC   Organization of Petroleum Exporting Countries; Arab-Israeli Conflict: OPEC temporarily cut off oil shipments to the United States in retaliation for American support of Israel.

5. Camp David Accords   Israel agreed to return the Sinai Peninsula to Egypt in return for recognition by Egypt. The agreement was brokered by the United States and settled at Camp David.

6. Palestinian Liberation Organization   Guerrilla force that vowed to fight until they could return to their homeland under a Palestinian government.

7. Office of Homeland Security   new cabinet-level post created by President George W. Bush to defend the United States against terrorism.

Name _____ Class _____ Date _____

CHAPTER

30 Section 4 Guided Reading and Review
A Global Economy

A. As You Read

Directions: As you read Section 4 in the textbook, fill in the missing causes and effects.

Causes	Effects
American companies pay workers higher wages than do companies in most other nations.	1. Foreign products are cheaper to manufacture and less expensive to buy than American products.
2. Congress ratified the North American Free Trade Agreement in 1993.	Trade boomed among Mexico, Canada, and the United States, and new jobs were created.
Environmental reformers called attention to the dangers of industrial waste and chemical pesticides.	3. The government began responding to concerns by passing laws to regulate waste and fight pollution.
A scientist dreamed of a vast inter-connected network of computers.	4. The Internet is a global source of electronic information and a means of communication.

B. Reviewing Key Terms

Directions: Briefly define each term.

5. trade deficit   situation in which a nation buys more goods and services from foreign countries than it sells to them

6. environmentalists   reformers who call attention to environmental dangers

7. renewable resource   a natural resource that can be replaced quickly by nature

8. global warming   a slow but steady rise in Earth's average temperature

9. Internet   a series of interconnected computers that gives users access to computerized information

10. e-commerce   business and trade over the Internet

CHAPTER

30 Section 5 Guided Reading and Review

New Challenges for the Nation

A. As You Read

Directions: As you read Section 5 in the textbook, answer the following questions:
Possible answers below

1. Why do so many Asians immigrate to the United States? _Wars and famines are pushing_ _them out of Asia. Others arrive seeking economic opportunity._

2. What is the function of the Immigration Reform and Control Act? _It allows those who_ _arrived in the United States illegally before 1982 to remain and apply for citizenship, and it imposes fines on those_ _who hire illegal aliens._

3. What is the current status of Native Americans? _Their population is growing; tribes and_ _organizations have greater self-governing power; reservations have worked to increase their economic independence._

4. What is the Americans with Disabilities Act? _This act outlaws discrimination in hiring against_ _those with physical or mental disabilities and requires employers to provide accommodations for disabled workers,_ _such as wheelchair ramps._

5. Why has the population of the United States grown older? _Birthrates have declined, and_ _medical care is improving._

6. What are two major challenges the United States faces in the twenty-first century?
terrorist attacks and illegal drug use

B. Reviewing Key Terms

Directions: Briefly define each term.

7. refugee _person who flees his or her homeland to seek safety elsewhere_

8. illegal alien _one who has entered a country without permission_

9. mainstreaming _placing children with special needs in regular classes_

EPILOGUE

 **Section 1 Guided Reading and Review**

Entering Modern Times

A. As You Read

Directions: As you read Section 1 in the textbook, answer the following questions:
Possible answers below

1. What were some of the reasons people moved west after the Civil War? _____
Mining and cattle ranching industries boomed. The government granted land to long-term settlers. Freedmen sought freedom they were denied in the South. Railroads granted easier access to the West.

2. What effect did the westward movement have on Native Americans? _____
They were pushed off their lands and forced onto reservations. Settlers killed the buffalo on which the lifestyle of the Plains Indians depended.

3. What effect did technology have on American industry after the Civil War? _____
Refrigeration, the telephone, the light bulb, and the electric power plant completely revitalized American industry, making it more productive and efficient.

4. What was the relationship between banks and corporations? _____
Banks invested heavily in corporations; therefore, bankers controlled company policies.

5. What are the arguments for and against monopolies? Against: They reduce competition, hurting small businesses and consumers. For: They mean lower production costs, lower prices, higher wages, and higher living standards.

6. What was the importance of the American Federation of Labor? _____
It was the first national organization of trade unions; it was a powerful ally of the worker.

7. What effect did immigrants have on American cities? Immigrants brought a great variety of languages, religions, and cultural customs to cities. Because of their numbers, cities grew rapidly.

B. Reviewing Key Terms

Directions: Briefly identify each of the following people.

8. Thomas Edison   inventor of the light bulb, the phonograph, and motion pictures

9. Andrew Carnegie   Scottish immigrant who worked on the railroads and later made a fortune in the steel industry

10. J. P. Morgan   banker who bought railroads and steel companies, president of US Steel, America's first billionaire

11. John D. Rockefeller   owned Standard Oil, a monopoly of oil refineries

EPILOGUE

 **Section 2 Guided Reading and Review**

A New Role for the Nation

A. As You Read

Directions: As you read Section 2 in the textbook, complete the following sentences:

Possible answers below

1. The Progressive Era gets its name from reforms intended to improve society for everyone.

2. The Sixteenth Amendment was important because it gave Congress the power to impose an

   income tax.

3. Theodore Roosevelt's reforms included enforcing antitrust acts against monopolies, supporting

   organized labor, conserving natural resources, and regulating foods and medicines for safety.

4. United States foreign policy began changing because overseas trade was expanding.

5. Roosevelt's statement that the United States had a right to intervene in Latin American

   affairs became known as the Roosevelt Corollary.

6. America declared war on Germany because Germany threatened international democracy.

B. Reviewing Key Terms

Directions: Match each term with its definition.

Column I	Column II
_a_ 7. muckraker	a. crusading journalist
_c_ 8. isolationism	b. control of several countries by one country
_b_ 9. imperialism	c. limited involvement in world affairs

EPILOGUE

Section 3 Guided Reading and Review

The Great Depression and World War II

A. As You Read

Directions: As you read Section 3 in the textbook, fill in details about each decade in American life. *Possible answers below*

1920s: The Jazz Age

1. widespread prosperity; mass production of the first automobiles; new independence for women; popularity of jazz music; many people buying on credit; stock market crash of 1929

1930s: The Great Depression

2. banks closed, unemployment was high; President Roosevelt's New Deal meant relief for the unemployed, plans for recovery, and reforms; building of many public works; government grew bigger

---

1940s: World War II

3. The United States entered the war in 1941 when Japan attacked Pearl Harbor; factories converted to war production; women took many industrial jobs as men went overseas to fight; Japanese Americans were put into relocation camps; the first atomic bombs were dropped.

B. Reviewing Key Terms

Directions: Briefly define each term. Note whether it applies to the 1920s, 1930s, or 1940s.

4. flapper   1920s; independent woman who wore short skirts and behaved recklessly

5. jazz   1920s; original American music style

6. margin buying   1920s; buying on credit

7. Social Security   1930s; government program that provided money for disabled or retired workers

8. Holocaust   1940s; massacre of millions of European Jews

9. deficit spending   1930s; spending more than one earns

Name _____ Class _____ Date _____

EPILOGUE

 # Section 4 Guided Reading and Review
The Cold War and the Civil Rights Era

A. As You Read

Directions: As you read Section 4 in the textbook, fill in the missing causes and effects.
Possible answers below

Causes	Effects
Soviet leaders indicated their intent to spread communism throughout the world.	1. The United States engaged in a Cold War to prevent the spread of communism.
2. The battles of World War II left Europe in ruins.	The Marshall Plan allotted $12 billion to help Europe recover.
Communist Fidel Castro seized control of Cuba.	3. Thousands of Cubans fled to the United States.
4. African Americans were denied their constitutional rights for nearly a century after the Civil War.	People fought for African American rights in the civil rights movement.
5. Americans agreed to boycott grapes.	The United Farm Workers gained better working conditions.
More and more American troops were sent to Vietnam.	6. More and more Americans protested the war.

B. Reviewing Key Terms

Directions: Briefly explain each person's role in the Cold War/Civil Rights era.

7. Fidel Castro   leader of Cuban Revolution; communist

8. John F. Kennedy   American President who supported civil rights, invaded Cuba in 1961, avoided war with the USSR, and committed troops to Vietnam

9. Rosa Parks   refused to give up her bus seat; inspired the successful Montgomery bus boycott

10. Martin Luther King, Jr.   southern minister; leader of civil rights movement; gave inspirational "I Have a Dream" speech in Washington, D.C.

11. Lyndon Johnson   American President; passed important civil rights legislation; committed troops to Vietnam

12. César Chavez   organized migrant workers and helped them win better working conditions

EPILOGUE

 **Section 5 Guided Reading and Review**

Into the Future

A. As You Read

Directions: As you read Section 5 in the textbook, answer the following questions:

Possible answers below

1. Why was Richard Nixon threatened with impeachment? <u>Nixon had tried to cover up the</u>
   <u>truth about his connection to a break-in at the Democratic national headquarters.</u>

2. What were the goals of the conservatives who supported Ronald Reagan? _____
   <u>They wanted a smaller federal government, less federal regulation of business, a focus on morality, and a return to</u>
   <u>traditional family values.</u>

3. What actions did Reagan take as president? <u>He cut taxes, slowed spending on social programs,</u>
   <u>eliminated many regulations on business, and increased military spending.</u>

4. What were some of Bill Clinton's presidential policies? <u>He supported social programs and</u>
   <u>legislation that protected the environment; he balanced the federal budget.</u>

5. How did the Cold War end? <u>Communist governments in Eastern Europe began to collapse; the Soviet</u>
   <u>Union broke apart into independent republics.</u>

6. What are some of the new challenges facing the United States? <u>competition for trade,</u>
   <u>how to protect the environment; how to deal with rising immigration; fighting global terrorism</u>

B. Reviewing Key Terms

Directions: Briefly define each term.

7. Watergate affair <u>break-in at Democratic national headquarters; President Nixon and his advisors tried to</u>
   <u>cover it up, and Nixon was later threatened with impeachment</u>

8. détente <u>a relaxation of tension between the Soviet Union and the United States</u>

9. North American Free Trade Agreement <u>reduction of trade barriers among the three nations of</u>
   <u>North America</u>